The
Biological
Way of Thought

MORTON BECKNER

The

Biological

Way of Thought

NEW YORK

COLUMBIA UNIVERSITY PRESS 1959

This study, prepared under the Graduate Faculties of
Columbia University, was selected by a committee of those
Faculties to receive one of the Clarke F. Ansley awards
given annually by Columbia University Press.

COPYRIGHT © 1959 COLUMBIA UNIVERSITY PRESS, NEW YORK
PUBLISHED IN GREAT BRITAIN, CANADA, INDIA, AND PAKISTAN
BY THE OXFORD UNIVERSITY PRESS
LONDON, TORONTO, BOMBAY, AND KARACHI
Library of Congress Catalog Card Number: 59-6061
MANUFACTURED IN THE UNITED STATES OF AMERICA

Preface

One often finds philosophers remarking that the account of scientific methods and procedures drawn up by contemporary empiricists suffers from an undue preoccupation with the physical sciences. The results, according to the contention, are a distorted picture of the total scientific endeavor, a misrepresentation of actual practice —perhaps even of the aims—of science, and a complete neglect of techniques of explanation and theory formation that are of great importance in the biological and social sciences. This book is the outcome of an attempt to examine the view by exhibiting certain modes of concept formation and explanation in biology that, it seems to me, have either been neglected or else not adequately analyzed.

Even though the book is concerned solely with questions of method, and accordingly contains no new empirical material, I hope that it may be useful to the scientist. I presuppose, of course, that even the treatment of substantive questions can be aided through a familiarity with methodology.

I would like to thank Professors Ernest Nagel, Albert Hofstadter, and John Cooley of Columbia University for their attention to many of the ideas in this book. Their critical and sympathetic discussions have been of immeasurable help to me, both in rejecting many wind-eggs and in attaining some degree of clarity and precision in whatever significant ideas remain. I am responsible, however, for the shortcomings of the final version.

I wish also to thank the University of Chicago Press, for their kind permission to reproduce materials from N. Rashevsky, *Mathematical Biophysics* (1948), and Routledge and Kegan Paul Ltd. for theirs to quote from J. H. Woodger, *Biological Principles* (1948).

Claremont, California　　　　　　　　　MORTON BECKNER
June, 1958

Contents

CHAPTER I

Introduction

In a discussion of his reasons for recommending the search for "purely biological" explanations, J. H. Woodger compares the contemporary biologist to a Kepler whose Tycho has overwhelmed him with data that are both too abundant and too exact.[1] Biology is therefore a science that was "born too late, when the means of observation have become too perfect."[2] Although Woodger does not explicitly draw the distinction, he evidently thinks that two factors are involved in the lateness of the birth of biological theory. The first is the existence of a body of biological data, already large and incessantly growing larger, that has not as yet been interpreted by means of a systematic application of general principles. The second is the biologist's knowledge that whatever else they may be, the systems which he studies are physicochemical systems. This knowledge, Woodger believes, has in practice retarded the development of a theoretical biology by drawing the investigator's attention from the "characteristically biological" aspects of organisms,[3] and by endowing him with a methodological bias that presents an actual obstacle to the development of a "biological way of thinking."[4] In these remarks, Woodger has summed up the plight of the modern biologist, as he is seen from the point of view both of vitalism and of organismic biology: the biologist is confronted with more data than he can handle, and he has not freed himself from a bias that would allow development of theories and methods that would enable him to handle them.

An examination of the "biological way of thinking" that is in fact employed in dealing with the problems that led Woodger to describe the plight of biology in this way constitutes the body of the

[1] Woodger, *Biological Principles,* pp. 317–18.
[2] Poincaré, *Science and Hypothesis,* p. 181. Cited in Woodger, *Biological Principles,* p. 318.
[3] Woodger, *Biological Principles,* p. 318.   [4] *Ibid.,* p. 325.

present study. For biology is not merely a compendium of statements about the natural history of organisms; nor is it a branch of physics, chemistry, or even physiology, the opinions of some physiologists notwithstanding. In this obvious sense, biology is in practice an autonomous discipline: ecology, morphology, paleontology, genetics, etc., are certainly not identical, in respect to concepts and principles used, with any recognized branch of physics or chemistry. Our task will be to uncover and investigate the logical features that are characteristic of the biological way of thinking, and to determine whether these features are peculiar to biological theory.

Much has been written in the past thirty years about the damage done to biology by a too exclusive attention to the physicochemical aspect of organic phenomena; I shall not retrace that well-trodden ground. However, the empirical problems that gave rise to the controversy between "vitalists" and "mechanists" are still with us, though nowadays they are discussed in other terms. In particular, the same problems that led to Driesch's theory of entelechies directing embryonic development and instinctive behavior have given rise to the movement known as "organismic biology": a movement supported by writers on the whole more cautious and more skeptical than the early vitalists. I shall examine the way in which the doctrines and methodological proposals of organismic biology may be interpreted as methods of dealing with classes of biological phenomena, and I shall try to show that these methods are well-founded. Organismic biology will be treated not as a critical doctrine directed against opponents with an inadequate "mechanistic" or "additive" point of view, but as a positive attempt to come to grips with real problems. Special attention will be given to the organismic biologists because, in their methodological writings, they have consistently singled out those aspects of biological phenomena whose treatment seems, at least prima facie, to require methods of study not employed in the physical sciences, and have made constructive attempts to formulate the principles of these methods. This study is not an examination of organismic biology, but an examination of the parts of biological theory that are magnified in the organismic biologist's perspective.

I have tried to be guided by conservative maxims, i.e., to assume, unless contrary evidence proved to be conclusive, that *sui generis* methods are not required in biology. Accordingly, my interpretations of biological theory rely heavily, both in general outlook and in matters of detail, on the work done by philosophers of science who either have been concerned with the principles of scientific knowledge as a whole, or have worked out their views with the physical sciences primarily in mind. In some cases I would be unwilling to vouch for the acceptability of the offered interpretations in the eyes of the organismic biologists.

Three closely related theses will be defended and expanded:

The characteristic doctrines of organismic biology involve methodological proposals for investigating the behavior of systems whose structural complexity precludes, at least at the present time, explanation in physicochemical terms; these proposals include a statement of the conditions under which relevant factors may safely be simplified or ignored altogether.

Much of contemporary biological theory does exhibit the methods and results recommended by organismic biologists.

When we state the empirical conditions, and make explicit the circumstances of an epistemological nature, under which the proposals of organismic biologists may profitably be followed, it can be seen that these conditions and circumstances are characteristic of regions of biology (and indeed of other sciences) that have not been of primary concern to organismic biologists. In addition, they make appropriate modes of concept formation and of explanation that are widespread in biological theory, but which are not ordinarily associated with the organismic biologist's position.

Let us examine these three theses more closely.

THE DOCTRINES OF ORGANISMIC BIOLOGY

We must first state in summary form the doctrines that are characteristic of organismic biology. It should be noted that organismic biologists tend to be vaguest at just those points which are most crucial for an understanding of their point of view. What is lacking in clarity, perhaps, is often compensated by continued reiteration of the point in various terms and from a variety of standpoints, so

that the sympathetic reader may be convinced that the points are
well taken, however much he might wish for greater clarity. Further, we may say that organismic biologists are unclear as to
whether the properties they ascribe to organisms are supposed to be
peculiar to organisms and other organic systems, or whether they
are maintaining the more modest thesis that these properties, while
they are not peculiar to organisms, are in fact possessed by them,
and are to be ignored only at great peril. By seeming to maintain
the former thesis in certain cases (E. S. Russell and L. von
Bertalanffy, for example, argue respectively that the "directiveness"
and peculiar "historical character" of organisms are unparalleled in
the inorganic world), organismic biologists open themselves unnecessarily to what appears to be a piecemeal refutation of their
whole position: if it is shown that, when the necessary clarifications
are made, there is no reason to regard, e.g., directiveness and historical character as peculiar properties of the organic, the in-
sistent call for a unique method of treatment would appear to be
based on a misunderstanding. But if no more than the latter thesis
is maintained, the organismic biologist need not subject himself to
this criticism. If these properties are possessed by organic systems,
and are in fact neglected by biologists, then an examination of the
properties, and their consequences for method, could conceivably
have all the salutary effects that the organismic biologist would
wish. Indeed, a frank admission of inorganic analogies with the
organic may suggest, and in fact often has suggested, fruitful
methods for the biologist—methods previously established in the
physical sciences.

Organismic biologists do not in general maintain that certain
properties of organic systems are ignored by other biologists, but
only that, in certain contexts, these properties are not given due
weight. Consequently, any list of doctrines attributed to organismic
biologists will include points that at least some other biologists
have explicitly noted, and perhaps even emphasized. Organismic
biology, then, differs from nonorganismic biology in that its proponents engage in a systematic logical examination of these trou-
blesome properties of organic systems, relating them one to another,
and drawing general morals for biological thought. (Incidentally,

organismic biologists fire long and carefree volleys at theories which they regard as jointly inadequate and nonorganismic.)

We shall now summarize under four headings the characteristic doctrines of organismic biology.

ORGANIZING RELATIONS. It is argued that the living organism, and some of its parts, exhibit levels of organization above the physico-chemical level; and that whereas the organism doubtless consists entirely of chemical constituents, these constituents are organized in such a way that the wholes composed of these constituents exhibit behavior and properties that are not chemical. An example of such a whole is a system of chromosomes within a cell. Each chromosome may well be a chain of macromolecules or an aperiodic crystal, but the physics and chemistry of macromolecules and crystals contain no statements about *some* of the properties of chromosome systems that are of interest to the biologist, e.g., that the chromosomes segregate by pairs during meiosis, or that duplication of a chromosome part in a Drosophila gamete may result in an adult fly possessing abnormally large eyes. These properties are dependent not only on the organization of the chromosome system, but on the organization of the cell, and in the latter example, of the entire organism. As the term "organismic biology" implies, special emphasis is placed upon those wholes which are ordinarily called organisms, *viz.*, individual plants, animals, and perhaps viruses. The concept of "organization" is correlative to the concept of "whole"; parts constitute wholes, not merely by virtue of spatiotemporal continuity, but by virtue of the organizing relations between the parts. To a considerable extent, the organismic biologist's writing is concerned with explaining these two concepts, and showing why it is necessary to treat some systems as wholes. Often it is said that the properties of the part are determined by,[5] or must be explained in terms of, the whole. It is sometimes held that the whole cannot be explained in terms of its parts, or even that in some sense the whole is more than the sum of its parts. We shall have occasion to consider these contentions after we have examined some of the methods employed by biologists (of whatever "school") in dealing with the problem of organization.

[5] Haldane, *Mechanism*, pp. 79, 86. Cited in Woodger, *Biological Principles*, pp. 246–47.

DIRECTIVENESS. Whatever the organizing relations between the parts of organic wholes or unities may be, one aspect of their organization is the fact that the whole possesses or is capable of "directiveness." This directiveness is understood to include the relation between structure and function, goal-directed behavior, and behavior that subserves any of the biological "ends" of maintenance, reproduction, or development.[6] The problem of directiveness (or teleology—I shall use the traditional term) is recognized to be only one, though perhaps the major, aspect of the general problem of biological organization. We shall raise the question of whether or not the fact that organisms exhibit "directiveness"—organismic biologists always define "directiveness" or its synonyms in such a way that we can be sure it exists—requires the biologist to use modes of explanation that differ ultimately from explanations in the physical sciences. We shall conclude that it does not, but that it makes useful a mode of explanation that differs penultimately from *most* explanations in the physical sciences.

HISTORICITY. Many biologists, and not only those who have associated themselves explicitly with the "organismic point of view," have declared that some of the special methodological problems of biological theory arise from the fact that organisms, as well as other organic systems, possess a "historical character" or "aspect."[7] Different writers, and some writers at different times, seem to include each of the following facts about organic systems under the heading of "historical character": (*a*) All organic systems have histories, and part of the duty of the biologist is to give a descriptive account of these histories; e.g., paleontology describes the successive changes in form of groups of organisms, and embryology describes the normal changes that characterize the histories of individual organisms. (*b*) The past of an organic system determines, or helps to determine, its present structure and behavior. (*c*) Many types of organic change, e.g., ontogeny, regeneration, and evolution, are serial or irreversible. (*d*) Many organic changes are properly described by the term "development." "Development" includes growth, elabora-

[6] See Russell, *Directiveness*, pp. 5–6, 9, 80; and Von Bertalanffy, *Modern Theories*, pp. 8–10.
[7] Woodger, *Biological Principles*, pp. 394–402; Von Bertalanffy, *Modern Theories*, p. 175; Mainx, *Foundations of Biology*, pp. 30–34, 42.

tion, and differentiation, accompanied by the appearance of new potentialities at a higher level of organization.[8] This occurs in both ontogeny and phylogeny. (*e*) Finally, the course of development from germ to adult organism is determined in part by the past history of the ancestors of the organism. Thus the properties of a contemporary system, e.g., the capacity to develop a fetal membrane, are dependent upon a number of occurrences that happened in the geological past and involved a large class of systems that are distinct from the contemporary system, although related to it in the relation of ancestor to descendant. Although ontogeny does not recapitulate phylogeny in the thoroughgoing manner envisaged by Haeckel, such recapitulation phenomena involving the parts of organisms, and characteristics of their parts, are common; and nonrecapitulatory phenomena are influenced in various ways by the past historical course of phylogeny.

These five facts include, I think, everything that organismic biologists include under the head of the "historical character" of organisms. Evidently, not all of them present problems that are peculiar to biological theory. Many sciences are concerned with a descriptive account of the past history of the objects that constitute their subject matter; the present behavior of all systems is influenced by their past; and all systems exhibit some changes that are irreversible. It is, however, possible to define "development" in such a way that only organic systems show it, e.g., as Woodger does,[9] so that development presents a problem peculiar to biological theory. Naturally it would not then follow that the problem of development requires methods of treatment found nowhere in the inorganic sciences: a unique problem does not entail a unique method of solution, but only a unique solution. Woodger's analysis of development includes reference to a particular type of organization—what he calls the "cell-type of organization"—and therefore, since only biologists are professionally interested in cells, we may say that development is a peculiarly biological problem by this definition. The final fact included under the "historical character" of organisms, however, con-

[8] Von Bertalanffy, *Modern Theories*, pp. 175, 181–82; and Woodger, *Biological Principles*, pp. 358, 372.
[9] Woodger, *Biological Principles*, pp. 338–42, 372–73.

stitutes a special problem for biology, and not merely by virtue of a special definition. As Von Bertalanffy puts it, "the germ as we see it before us is a structure which in its faculties has been collected in geological times. Moreover, this historical accumulation, and the progressive evolution of these collected faculties in the course of individual development, is not comparable with any other process in the world." [10] We shall examine some of the logical problems of explanation raised by this situation.

THE AUTONOMY OF BIOLOGICAL THEORY. The fourth doctrine of organismic biology is not a theory about organisms, but a partly descriptive, partly prescriptive observation about biological theory. It is the assertion that biology has to some extent developed laws and concepts of its own, and ought to expend a greater amount of effort in developing and elaborating such laws and concepts. Involved in this assertion is the view that biology should rid itself of "limitations imposed by the materialistic and mechanistic hypotheses," [11] and should examine the organism without prejudice, preconception, or unconscious bias,[12] in order to discover and relate the properties it has *qua* living organism. The biologist need not feel that he has missed the mark if his concepts are not definable in physicochemical terms, or if the mechanisms he posits for the sake of explanation (e.g., "organizers," "organ forming fields") are not physicochemical mechanisms. The fact of biological organization makes it appropriate to use concepts that describe and relate the *relata* on the higher levels of organization.[13] In short, the biologist may legitimately and profitably use "specifically biological" concepts and laws,[14] and must use them in order to do justice to his subject matter. Woodger emphasizes the existence of higher levels of organization, in particular, of hierarchical organization, as requiring specifically biological concepts and laws; Russell, Von Bertalanffy, and J. S. Haldane place emphasis upon the teleological character of organisms. Von Bertalanffy, for example, says that "the

[10] Von Bertalanffy, *Modern Theories*, pp. 181–82.
[11] Russell, *Directiveness*, p. 3.
[12] *Ibid.*; Woodger, *Biological Principles*, p. 319.
[13] Woodger, *Biological Principles*, p. 319.
[14] Russell, *Directiveness*, pp. 4, 9; Von Bertalanffy, *Modern Theories*, p. 181; Haldane, *Mechanism*, p. 77; and Von Bertalanffy, *Problems of Life*, p. 151.

real biological problem lies just in this question of the significance of organs and vital processes for the organism." [15]

I shall argue that these four points are indeed well taken, and that the first three do indicate regions of biology in which the injunctions contained in the fourth may be pursued with profit. It will be necessary to make clearer the properties of organisms that are meant by terms such as "organization," "directiveness," "wholeness," and "historical character," and to see what bearing the possession of these properties by organic systems has on the organismic biologist's claim that biology is an autonomous discipline with concepts and laws peculiar to itself. I think that no special problem of method is raised as long as we consider these properties as descriptive categories. But as soon as we raise the question of explanation of biological organization and directiveness, or rather of particular biological phenomena that exhibit organization or directiveness, or the kind of dependence upon past historical occurrences shown in ontogeny, questions of method are raised. This is not because these properties are unparalleled in the inorganic world, or in some sense are "irreducible" to inorganic properties, but because the systems which possess them do in fact exhibit relations with each other and relations among their parts that may be explained while abstracting from, or, more accurately, simply ignoring the underlying physico-chemical mechanisms. It is by stating the conditions under which this abstraction is useful and showing how the types of explanation that result are similar to and differ from other types of explanations that organismic biology may be freed from the charge that it is merely speculative, overly vague, or is nothing more than an elaboration of the obvious.

I have found it desirable to treat the methods of dealing with the higher levels of organization, and with historicity and teleology, from two distinct points of view. On the one hand, I have examined some of the *concepts* employed in theories concerned with these problems, in order to discover their characteristic logical function— their "geography." A classification of the concepts peculiarly suited

[15] Von Bertalanffy, *Modern Theories*, p. 10. See also in this connection Russell, *Directiveness*, pp. 4, 9; and Haldane, *Mechanism*, p. 77.

for these functions, together with the technical distinctions and definitions necessary for their description are presented in Chapter II. The results of these analyses are subsequently applied in the interpretation of systematics or taxonomy and in that of the general problems of historicity and teleology.

On the other hand, the logical character and functions of modes of *explanation* of higher-level phenomena have been examined. Organization is of course a fact about systems that no one would deny; and in many contexts organization presents no "problem," but is taken as a matter of course. The physicist, for example, makes no fuss about organization, but he must take it into account, e.g., in deciding which form of the law of conservation of energy to apply in a given system. Organization constitutes a problem only under very special epistemological conditions, namely, when the phenomena to be explained are excessively complex when analyzed with the help of principles and concepts of an established theory known to be applicable to the phenomena. This last clause contains the crucial point: organization emerges as a problem when there is too much knowledge in one direction and too little in another. In this sense, organization is a methodological category, not exclusively an ontological one. Moreover, the "complexity" of phenomena and even of the systems showing them, is not simply an ontological fact, but is relative to the theory utilized in their analysis. In short, the problem of organization is a problem of simplification, or better, a problem of finding "certain key-factors and vantage points" (to use Needham's phrase [16]) which provide principles and concepts relative to which the phenomena or systems under investigation are not complex. I have, then, interpreted the concepts and explanations characteristic of the "biological way of thinking" (the import of the term "characteristic" will be investigated later) as accessory tools in the task of simplifying phenomena that are complex, even prohibitively complex, from the point of view of physical and chemical theories. The concept of a model has proved very useful in the analysis of the explanation of these phenomena. Chapter III is devoted to an exposition of a theory of the functions of the type of model employed in dealing with organization. Thus the succeeding

[16] Needham, "Mechanistic Biology," in *Science,* ed. Needham, p. 245.

two chapters are concerned with laying the foundation for considering biological theory proper.

ORGANISMIC BIOLOGY AND
CONTEMPORARY BIOLOGICAL THEORY

When the empirical claims and methodological recommendations of organismic biology are interpreted respectively as the outcome and application of methods of simplifying the analysis of systems possessing, from alternative points of view, a high degree of complexity, and explaining the phenomena they exhibit, organismic biology, as a "school of thought," can be seen in relation to other schools, and, more importantly, in relation to the work of the many biologists in museums, the field, and laboratories who are not associated with any particular movement. If organismic biology is more than pure speculation, it must have relevance to the actual practice of working biologists, taking into account their methods and problems, and offering interpretations of at least some aspects of the body of biological accomplishments. I shall maintain that biology does show an awareness of the problems of organization, directiveness, and historicity, and that the methodological proposals of organismic biology are implicitly followed in dealing with these problems. In other words, I shall try to show that organismic biology is less a school of thought, a revolutionary movement bent on thoroughgoing reform, than a movement that emphasizes selected parts of biological theory, and proposes a deepening and extension of certain methods of concept formation and explanation that are in fact already widely employed. Without doubt, many organismic biologists have been seized with the spirit of reform; for example, D'Arcy Thompson has declared that J. S. Haldane is not merely trying to reform biology, but is attempting to reform the thought of the world.[17] Woodger, as I understand his *Biological Principles*, would like to revolutionize the thought of the world along Whiteheadian lines. This spirit, however valuable it may be by way of arousing biologists from unwarranted complacency, has led organismic biologists to exaggerate the gap between themselves and the remainder

[17] Thompson, review of *The New Physiology*, by Haldane, *Mind*, N.S., XXVII, 359. Cited in Woodger, *Biological Principles*, p. 247.

of the biological community. This is one reason for the insistence that organisms are unique in the world in just those respects that entail unique methods of investigation.[18]

One feels that organismic biology would like to rest its case for a new method on the proof that organisms are different in kind from inorganic systems: this is a double mistake, since the possession by a system of a unique property is certainly not sufficient grounds for postulating a special method of study; and if organisms do possess a property or properties that call for special methods of study, a call for the pursuit of these methods is perfectly warranted, even if the properties are shown by inorganic systems, especially if it is true, as organismic biologists assert, that these methods have been too much neglected.

The fact that organismic biology is less revolutionary than its proponents might seem to claim should not lead us to detract from the value and importance of their views; but we are not here concerned with defending the position, or with reaffirming any differences between its doctrines and the views of orthodox biology, but only with an attempt to understand the position in the light of the problems of biology. Therefore, this work approaches certain problems of biological theory—the problems of teleology, organization, and historicity—by way of an analysis of the actual methods used in dealing with them; and in addition it is shown that organismic biology may be interpreted in such a way that its doctrines amount to an emphasis upon these methods.

THE EXTENSION OF ORGANISMIC METHODS

If indeed the methods and "way of thinking" emphasized by organismic biology are exemplified in orthodox biology, we should expect them to appear in regions of biology that have not been of primary concern to organismic biologists. Vitalism, which was in many respects the forerunner of modern organismic biology, took the problems of embryological development and of animal instinct as examples of phenomena showing the characteristics that were so mysterious from a "mechanistic" point of view. Driesch postulated

[18] For examples of this insistence, see Haldane, *Mechanism*, pp. 94–95; Russell, *Directiveness*, pp. 4–5; Von Bertalanffy, *Modern Theories*, pp. 181–82.

two kinds of entelechy operating in embryogeny and instinct, "morphogenetic" and "psychoid" entelechies. Today, embryogeny, together with the phenomena of regeneration, repair, and metamorphosis, are the problems with which organismic biologists are most at home. The problem of instinct, though not ignored, has passed into the background, except in so far as instincts, like physiological processes, are regarded as adaptive. Von Bertalanffy regards the problem of development as the *"paradigma* of the problem of life." [19] The term "organismic biology" indicates this emphasis upon the level of organization that gives rise to properties characterizing the single whole organism. Organization is of course exhibited at other levels than that of the single whole organism. There are organized parts of organisms, and various types of supraorganismic systems, e.g., the interbreeding population, the colony, biocoenoses, systems in symbiosis, etc. I shall consider, for the most part, levels of organization above the organismic level, but the principles of concept formation and explanation are not restricted to those levels.

The analysis of concepts will be applied in interpreting systematics—that fundamental branch of biology in which organization first presents itself as a problem—morphology, ethology, or the study of animal instinct, and evolution theory. I distinguish two types of "teleological explanation" and two types of "genetic explanation," and employ the theory of models as well as the theory of concepts in discussing their logical features. A chapter is devoted to the logic of explanations in neo-Darwinian evolution theory, in part because of its great intrinsic interest, and in part because the theory exhibits all of the types of concepts and explanations with which I have been concerned, and illustrates their interconnections. Finally, in the concluding chapter, I draw together the threads of the argument in so far as they apply to organismic biology.

[19] Von Bertalanffy, *Modern Theories,* p. 68.

CHAPTER II

Types of Biological Concepts

Those who urge that biology is or ought to be an autonomous discipline claim that biology does or ought to work with concepts which are "distinctively" or "specifically" biological. And indeed, this would seem to be a minimal condition of autonomy, since any investigation which revealed a new law statable in terms, say, of the concepts of physics, would surely have revealed just another physical law, however the term "physical" might be construed. It is the task of this chapter to discover whether in fact biology does contain "specific" and "distinctive" concepts, and if so, in what sense they are "distinctive": whether they are of types unique in biology, or merely widespread there and rare elsewhere, or are specifically biological just because biologists and no others employ them. I shall conclude that there are such concepts, that their function is just what organismic biologists have suggested, and that they possess logical features of considerable interest to the methodologist.

What is meant by saying that a concept is "distinctively biological," or, for that matter, distinctively "chemical," or "psychological"? Three possibilities suggest themselves. (1) The concept may be applied only to subject matters that are conventionally regarded as falling within the sphere of a particular science. Thus "embryo," "oxidation," and "motive" would be respectively biological, chemical, and psychological concepts in this sense. If organismic biologists meant no more than this, their claims could be interpreted only as an insistence that biology has a right to such concepts and need not restrict itself to those employed in physics and chemistry.[1]

[1] The following statement of Haldane's lends itself to this innocent interpretation: "I shall try to illustrate in physiology the case for studying respira-

Nowadays no one would deny this, but the warning might still have point if biologists who believe it nevertheless failed to act on it. In any case concepts which are "distinctive" in this sense raise no special problems of method. (2) Concepts distinctive of a science might be thought to serve functions that are peculiar to that science; e.g., specifically psychological concepts might be needed in explaining human creativity, or specifically biological concepts might be needed in the analysis of purposive activity. This possibility will require serious consideration. (3) It might be maintained that some sciences utilize concepts which have logical properties not or seldom possessed by concepts in other sciences, and that these properties are systematically related to distinctive features of that science's subject matter.

A concept may conceivably be distinctive of biology in all three senses, and if a concept is distinctive of biology in either of the last two senses, presumably it is also distinctive in the first. I shall maintain that there are many concepts in biology that are distinctive of it in the sense that they apply only to biological subject matters; they possess logical features which, though not confined to biological concepts, seldom characterize the concepts of the other natural sciences, and often do characterize the concepts of psychology and the social sciences; and they serve general functions that are not unique but are widespread in biological theory, whereas they are not widespread in the other natural sciences. If a concept meets these three conditions, it possesses reasonable claim to the title of "specifically biological."

By a "logical property" of a concept I understand either a mode of definition of the concept,[2] or a relationship between the definition of a concept and the technique or operations that warrant the concept's application. Three classes of distinctively biological concepts

---

tion in the light of distinctively biological conceptions, in the place of merely trying to study it in the light of physical and chemical conceptions." Haldane, *Philosophical Basis*, p. 47.

[2] Some writers have objected to the whole vocabulary of concepts for reasons that do not concern us here. I shall use the terminology; in particular, I shall speak of "defining" concepts; this is to be understood as defining the term which designates the concept. I shall also speak of the extension of concepts. Single quotes will be used to name terms, and double quotes to name concepts.

will be defined in terms of their logical properties; their functions will be examined in subsequent chapters.

LOGICAL PROPERTIES OF CONCEPTS

In order to describe the mode of definition of a concept, and the relation between mode of definition and the technique of application, a number of technical terms will be useful. Let us call a concept C "well-defined" whenever the following conditions are met:

1) A test-procedure may be described for determining whether or not any entity (this neutral term is intended to include particulars, relations, classes, events, and processes) is a member of its extension
2) The test-procedure consists of a finite number of logical and/or physical operations
3) Each operation of the test-procedure is compatible with the laws of nature and of logic

Any *definiens* for a concept C which renders C well-defined, i.e., from which a permissible test-procedure is deducible, with or without the aid of known laws of nature, will be called a "W-definition of C."

The notion of W-definition is intended to be an application of the verifiability criterion of meaningful propositions to concepts. As such it suffers from those difficulties that careful analysis has discovered in the criterion. It is admitted that there may be concepts, or at least pseudoconcepts, which we cannot unambiguously accept or reject as well-defined. Since my purpose is not to develop the concept of W-definition for the sake of a critical criterion applicable to all concepts, but only to provide a terminology for the precise description of a class of biological concepts, it is sufficient that the concept of W-definition apply unambiguously to the members of this class.

No restriction is placed upon the time at which the test-procedure of a W-definition may be carried out. It is evident that a concept may be W-defined, and yet useless for many scientific purposes. If the concept is to serve in a hypothesis it is necessary that its applicability be determinable at the time of the application of the hypothesis, and not merely at some future or past time.

Suitable restrictions on the admissibility of W-defined concepts will allow us to describe a class of concepts whose usefulness in empirical science is guaranteed—in so far as bare empirical content can guarantee usefulness. Let us call a concept C "effectively defined" with respect to a nonempty class K of entities if and only if:

1) C is W-defined; or else there are preestablished criteria of adequacy for any W-definition of C

2) K is included in (or identical with) the extension of C

3) A test-procedure, consisting of a finite number of operations, may be described for determining, with a high degree of probability, whether or not any entity is a member of K

4) Each operation of the test-procedure is known to be compatible with the laws of nature; and finally

5) The test-procedure can be carried out in the present

Any definition that renders a concept C effectively defined with respect to a class K will be termed an E_k-definition. If K and the extension of C coincide, the concept is E-defined without qualification.

The concept of W-definition, roughly speaking, involves a test-procedure whose operations are empirically possible, and which would yield a decision on any entity if it were applied to it. E- and E_k-definitions represent a strengthening of these conditions in some respects and a weakening in others: the test-procedure must not only be empirically possible, i.e., must not be incompatible with a law of nature, but must also be known to be empirically possible. This means that the test-procedure is formulated only with the aid of available theory. When available theory permits an investigator to decide that a given entity is a member of the extension of C only if it is in fact a member of a specifiable subclass K of this extension (as determined by a W-definition), then this test-procedure is not sufficiently powerful for effectively defining C, but may be powerful enough to lead to the exclusion from the class of C's most non-C's, and to the inclusion of most C's; but there remains an indeterminate residue. In traditional terms, we can say that this situation results from failure of the test-procedure to investigate properties common and peculiar to all C's; it investigates instead properties common and peculiar to a species of the genus C. Test-procedures of this nature yield, as I have stipulated, an E_k-definition, effective with respect to K.

The requirement that an E-definition must be applicable in the present needs no justification. It is clearly too strict a requirement if our purpose were to specify the conditions under which a concept would be said to possess empirical meaning; but, on the other hand, no scientist would be impressed if he were told that a theoretical term could be applied solely on the basis of evidence that would perforce be available only in the past or in the future.

Finally, it would be unreasonable to require that an E-defining test-procedure is an infallible instrument, even if correctly applied, for determining membership in K. There is of course the danger of error in the application of any step in an empirical test-procedure. These sources of error infect both W- and E-definitions, and do not concern us here. In stating that an E-definition determines membership in K with a high degree of probability, I mean that if the results of each step in the test-procedure are correctly interpreted, even then membership in K is not infallibly determined.

Not every E-definition of C is also a W-definition, although one may be, if the degree of probability assignable on correct application of the E-defining test-procedure is one. As remarked above, the converse is also true. Notice that an E- or E_k-definition may bear only a contingent relation to a W-definition of C, since the test-procedure of an E-definition may enjoin a search for properties that are constantly conjoined with the properties sought in carrying out the W-defining test-procedure.

There are concepts which possess (and others which lack) both W- and E-definitions. Moreover, a concept may possess either type of definition while lacking the other. The cases which will be of greatest interest to us are, first, those in which a concept is E-defined, but not W-defined, but for which there are preestablished criteria of adequacy for a W-definition. (Such criteria will be called the W-defining criteria or conditions of adequacy.) The second is the case in which the concept is W-defined, but which possesses no general E-definition because of inadequacies in the theory which could reasonably be expected to yield an E-defining test-procedure. In such cases there may exist a class of E_k-definitions such that the set-sum of all the K's does not fully exhaust the extension of the concept. In my opinion, these considerations are capable of shedding considerable light on the logic of concept formation in regions of biology largely neglected by students of this subject, especially on the logic of taxonomy and on the logic of the concepts employed in genetic and teleological explanation. This constitutes my primary motive for introducing the distinction. A second motive is to provide a terminology for describing the logical properties of concepts in terms of the relation between their W- and E-definitions. It is here that what is really distinctive of biological concepts may be revealed.

The definitions of all the so-called "effective" properties of logical formulae are both W- and E-definitions; the noneffective properties are neither W- nor E-defined. For example, in a logistic system with a decision-procedure, "theorem" is both W- and E-defined, but it is neither if there is no decision-procedure. It is clear, therefore, that there are concepts which are useful, but whose definitions fail to meet the rather stringent conditions of W- and E-definition. Such concepts will not concern us here.

An example of a concept that is W-defined but not E-defined is afforded by the notion of a "gene locus" on a chromosome. I will not formulate a W-definition, but I think it would be agreed that one could be found. No geneticist, however, would say that the concept is E-defined, since certain rather special conditions must be met in order to determine whether or not a given chromosome locus bears a gene. It is quite possible to formulate these conditions. Roughly, they are the conditions that make chromosome maps possible, e.g., some degree of heterozygosity and the occurrence of crossing over at meiosis. It is reasonable to assume that further advances in technique will render the concept fully E-defined.

Every disposition-predicate whose meaning may be partially specified by means of a bilateral reduction sentence is W-defined, since such a sentence states an operation which, if it is performed, yields a result that unambiguously determines the application of the predicate.[3] The question of what it means to say that an object possesses a disposition-predicate if no operation enjoined in a reduction sentence is applied to it may remain undecided so far as this analysis is concerned. An interesting complication, however, is af-

[3] Carnap, "Testability and Meaning," in *Philosophy of Science,* ed. Feigl and Brodbeck, pp. 52–53.

forded by disposition terms whose meaning cannot be specified by a bilateral reduction sentence, owing to the empirical impossibility of applying the test-procedure to all objects. This situation yields a concept that is not W-defined, but may be fully E-defined. Consider the embryological concept of a region of "prospective potency." Such a region is said to be, e.g., presumptive neural plate, if the cells in the region would in fact yield neural plate if the embryo developed normally. But this does not constitute a W-definition of "presumptive neural plate," since we are unable to deduce from it a procedure applicable to all embryos, but only to those which do in fact develop normally. Yielding neural plate is a sufficient condition, but not a necessary one, although it would be necessary also if the test-procedure could be performed in all cases. But it cannot always be performed. It is difficult to see what would count in this case as a W-definition, but we may specify a W-defining condition of adequacy, namely, that no region is to be termed presumptive neural plate if it does not yield neural plate in the course of normal development, and is to be so termed if it does.

In practice, "presumptive neural plate" is effectively defined as any embryonic region that shares a number of morphological features—especially location with respect to the axes of the embryo—with regions of embryos which have yielded neural plate in normal development. In this case K and the extension of the *definiendum* are identical, but the E-definition, even when its test-procedure is rigidly observed and carried out without error, assigns a region to K with a probability less than one, not with "definitional necessity." Of course, one can stipulate that this E-definition is to count as a W-definition of "presumptive neural plate," but then we would have a distinct concept, since it is logically possible that a region answer to the E-definition and not yield neural plate in normal development. Philosophers sometimes seem to think that the scientist makes such stipulations, but in this case he certainly would not. Roughly speaking, the scientist is interested in presumptive neural plate because it yields neural plate, not because it happens to have such-and-such morphological properties.

This example serves to bring out a hidden unclarity in the phrase "in the present" employed in the explication of "effective definition."

"The present" refers to a finite time interval. It is then legitimate to ask whether there is an upper limit to the time interval that may elapse beyond which we would no longer say that the test-procedure is being carried out "in the present." Could, for instance, the test-procedure for effectively determining the degree of adaptability of a species consist in observing its evolution for millennia? If the purpose of effective definition is to provide the scientist with concepts he can apply in his everyday work, we must find a way to describe more accurately what is to count as "the present." This may be done without undue arbitrariness simply by specifying that a set of operations for E-defining C may be performed "in the present" only if the time of performance is less than every interval required for the discovery of *explananda* to be explained with the help of any hypotheses in which C figures. Whether or not a proposed test-procedure renders a concept E-defined will, then, in general depend upon the kinds of uses to be made of the concept. The suggested E-definition of "presumptive neural plate" at least meets the requirement that the test-procedure be carried out in the present. If the concept were to be utilized only, for example, in the description of normal ontogeny, its E-definition as a region that yields neural plate would be perfectly adequate; but the concept has, or at least is intended to have, other uses. The experimental embryologist uses the concept of regions of prospective potency in the formulation of generalizations concerning, e.g., the behavior of transplanted regions that do not behave normally.

THREE CLASSES OF CONCEPTS

The distinction between W- and E-definitions does not in itself provide us with a distinction between "specifically biological" concepts and the concepts distinctive of other sciences which may or may not be employed by the biologist, but it does provide us with a means of describing classes of concepts that are characteristically biological in one sense and fully unique in biological theory in another. These classes of concepts I will term *polytypic, historical,* and *functional.*

The warning should perhaps be repeated that these concepts are not restricted to biological theory. It will appear that members of

each class are found in ordinary language and in other sciences, especially those that contain a large measure of natural history, e.g.,
astronomy, geology, and anthropology. Nor do all or even the most
important concepts of biological theory fall into these categories.
Nevertheless, polytypic, historical, and functional concepts do play
a large role in biology. In particular, they include, I believe, all of
the concepts that organismic biologists would insist upon calling
"distinctively biological." Moreover, their utility in biological theory
is derived from exactly those features of biological subject matter
that raise the interesting questions of biological methodology,
namely, the great complexity, the historical character, and the organization of biological systems. This is the sense in which these
concepts are characteristic of biological theory. In addition, the
polytypic, historical, and functional concepts that are employed in
biology are also distinctively biological in the sense that they are
defined by means of properties that are of professional interest only
to biologists. This may well be offering the organismic biologists
much less than they are asking for, but in any case I have found no
other way of interpreting and reconstructing their claims on this
point.

POLYTYPIC CONCEPTS. A class is ordinarily defined by reference to
a set of properties which are both necessary and sufficient (by stipulation) for membership in the class. It is possible, however, to define
a group K in terms of a set G of properties $f_1, f_2, \ldots, f_n$ in a different manner. Suppose we have an aggregation of individuals (we
shall not as yet call them a class) such that:

   1) Each one possesses a large (but unspecified) number of the
      properties in G
   2) Each f in G is possessed by large numbers of these individuals;
      and
   3) No f in G is possessed by every individual in the aggregate

By the terms of 3), no f is necessary for membership in this aggregate; and nothing has been said to either warrant or rule out the
possibility that some f in G is sufficient for membership in the aggregate. Nevertheless, under some conditions the members would and
should be regarded as a class K constituting the extension of a concept defined in terms of the properties in G. If n is large, all the

members of K will resemble each other, although they will not resemble each other in respect to a given f. If n is very large, it would
be possible to arrange the members of K along a line in such a way
that each individual resembles his nearest neighbors very closely
and his further neighbors less closely. The members near the ex-
tremes would resemble each other hardly at all, e.g., they might
have none of the f's in G in common. Wittgenstein has emphasized
the importance that concepts of this logical character assume in
ordinary language, especially in that small segment of ordinary language that contains the semantical concepts of "meaning," "referring," "description," etc. He points out that all the members of such
classes have a "family resemblance" to one another; he does not
suggest a general term for classes of this kind. We shall call a concept C "polytypic with respect to G" if and only if it is E-definable
in terms of the properties in G; its extension K meets conditions 1)
and 2) above; and the E-defining test-procedure is intended to discover whether or not condition 1) is met. If the extension K in fact
also meets condition 3), the concept will be said to be "fully polytypic with respect to G," or "fully polytypic" if G is understood.

There are two questions of interest to raise concerning polytypic
concepts (or classes). What logical features distinguish them from
classes that are customarily defined as Boolean functions of a set of
properties (or classes); and what is their methodological significance, i.e., what functions do they perform, and what general features of the subject matter make them useful?

In the case of monotypic concepts (concepts defined by reference
to a property which is necessary and sufficient for membership in
its extension), purely syntactical criteria guarantee the existence of
an extension. If, for example, we have a number of classes w, x,
y, . . . , any function of these classes (subject to certain type or
stratification restrictions) is itself a class: either a class of elements
or the null class. The satisfaction of syntactical requirements does
not, however, guarantee the existence of a polytypic class. Suppose
that a set G of properties f_1, f_2, . . . , f_n are enumerated, and suppose that a number k is chosen as the "large number" mentioned in
condition 1). Now if an individual has k or more of the f's in G, it
does not follow that it is a member of a polytypic class K, for we do

not yet know whether the f's in G meet condition 2). If condition
2) is not also met, there is no class polytypic with respect to G.
This point is important. To put it in other words, we might say that
even if every f in G effectively defines a nonempty class, we cannot
assign an individual to K simply by determining empirically whether
or not it is a member of the classes defined by the f's. In this respect
polytypic classes are sharply distinguished from monotypic classes.
In order to assign an individual to K, we must have a further item
of empirical information, namely, that the various f's are widely distributed in K. Moreover, in order to determine whether an object is
a member of a fully polytypic class, still more information is required, namely, that no f is universally distributed in the class. In
order to possess *these* data, we must possess either an enumeration
of the members of K, or a reasonable sample of it, which obviously
presupposes at least a rough criterion of membership in K prior to
its effective definition as a polytypic class. I will return subsequently
to this last point.

It is reasonable to ask whether a definition of a polytypic concept
is after all a *definition*, since it is certainly imprecise. The vague
term "large number" occurs twice in the definition; it would seem
therefore that whenever we are in doubt about what number is
"large" in these contexts, there will always be the possibility of
borderline cases. This is perfectly true, indeed it is an essential aspect of polytypic classes. For suppose that we do have an enumeration of the f's in G, and we know that there is a class of individuals
such that each f is widely distributed in it, and no f is universal
throughout it. Then, as soon as we let k represent the "large number
of f's" that each individual in K must have, we have provided ourselves with the means of defining K as a monotypic class. We can
form all the distinct classes that are the Boolean product of k members of G, and then say that x is a member of K if and only if it is
a member of the class which is the Boolean sum of these Boolean
products. In short, K would be the disjunction of all conjunctions
of k members of G. This function lays down a single condition which
is both necessary and sufficient for membership in K.

Nevertheless, it would be misleading to reconstruct the notion of
a polytypic class in this way. In a sense, the whole point of poly-

typic E-definition is to avoid committing oneself to a necessarily arbitrary delimitation of a class before a theoretically adequate definition can be found. The polytypic E-definition leaves open the possibility that, for every arbitrarily selected k, an individual may possess each f of a given set of f's, and still not be a member of K; or may lack one or more of the f's in each distinct set of k f's, and still be a member of K. The polytypic E-definition leaves the borderline between K and non-K indeterminate where there is no theoretical reason for drawing the borderline at a particular point. Polytypic concepts are sufficiently justified if only on the grounds of scientific economy: new knowledge can be utilized in applying polytypic concepts without the necessity of modifying their definitions.

Polytypic concepts are found in many branches of biological theory, but the clearest instances are afforded by taxonomy. In Chapter IV, I shall utilize the concept of a polytypic class in presenting an interpretation of the modern taxonomic point of view known as "the New Systematics." Some of the methodological justification for the use of polytypic concepts will be presented in that context; equally important justifications will be considered in the analysis of genetic and teleological explanation. An especially important case is found in concepts which are monotypic in W-definition, but are polytypic, or fully polytypic, with respect to the properties that the scientist normally investigates in applying the concept.

Polytypic E-definition may be utilized in the application of historical and functional concepts; I shall now indicate what I mean by these terms.

HISTORICAL CONCEPTS. If we describe a contemporary system by means of a historical concept, as I shall understand the term, we are presupposing that the system has actually had such and such a history. To call a plant "hybrid corn," for example, is to presuppose that the plant is a first filial descendant of a cross between two distinct strains of corn, in the sense that if it is in fact not such a descendant, it is logically impossible for it to be hybrid corn. Illustrations of this type of concept may be found in all the branches of biology, but, as one might expect, they are especially common in those branches that deal with the histories of groups of organisms. A brief list from genetics and evolution theory will indicate the extent of historical concepts in the technical vocabulary of these sciences: mutation, polyploid, back-cross, kinship, homology, orthogenesis, convergence, rudimentation, relict, genetic drift, hypertely, and so on.

To state the definition formally: a concept C is said to be "historical" whenever either of the following two conditions are satisfied:

1) There exists a W-definition of C, or W-defining criteria of adequacy, such that any application of C to a system is necessarily false unless a set P of events have occurred prior to the time that C applies to the system

2) C is applied to a historical process; and there exists a W-definition of C, or W-defining criteria of adequacy, such that any application of C to a process is necessarily false unless the process undergoes a temporal sequence of stages (p_1, $p_2, \ldots, p_n) = P$

We may thus distinguish two types of historical concept: "hybrid" is an instance of the former; "hybridization," of the latter. If we term the members of P the "P-events of concept C," we may describe a common relation between pairs of historical concepts as follows: if C designates a *product*, the P-events of C are the P-events of a corresponding concept C′ which designates the *process* which yields that product. The first type of historical concept, to use traditional terminology, is a relation whose converse domain is prior in time to its domain; the latter is a property which is predicable only of a certain kind of particular, *viz.*, processes.

Historical concepts are of course legion in ordinary language. Here they serve the purposes of historical narration ("Veterans were voted a bonus") and explanation ("He was deported because he failed to become a citizen").[4] Historical concepts serve a like function of economy in historical narration and speculation in the sciences, but the important methodological question is this: What role, if any, do they play in the theory proper of a science? This question is closely related to the more general issue of the status of historical laws, and the nature of genetic or historical explanation. These questions will be discussed in Chapter V. For the present we are not

[4] I am assuming that "citizen" and "veteran" are W-defined in the law in terms of historical antecedents.

concerned with the detailed consideration of the uses of these concepts.

FUNCTIONAL CONCEPTS. The following definition of "functional concept" is intended as an explication of what some writers have called "teleological concepts," i.e., concepts which in some sense involve reference to a use or purpose or contribution made. I shall call a concept C "functional" if and only if C is W-defined (or, if not W-defined, possesses a W-defining condition of adequacy) such that every application of C to a system s or process F is (logically) false unless there exists a system s' and process F' (other than s and F) and at least one environment and state of s' in which s' does exhibit F', and in which s' would not exhibit F' if (1) F failed to occur, or (2) s is not a part of s' or that environment.[5] Under these conditions the class of s's and F's, when they are defined as the extensions of functional concepts, will be said to "contribute" to the "function" F'. Of course, a particular F or s may not contribute to the performance of F', if s' is never in the requisite state or environment. If s or F is a necessary condition of F' (i.e., in every environment), we have a special case of the "contribution" relation. The definition provides for the general case in which F' is never performed, or is performed in the absence of F or s. For example, assume that "photosynthesis" is a functional concept. Photosynthesis contributes to the growth of algae in all of their normal environments, but algae will grow in the dark in a suitable culture medium. Of course, some of the products of photosynthesis are necessary without qualification for the growth of algae.

Even though a particular object, a vacuum tube, for example, in fact contributes to a function, such as voltage regulation, the concept of a vacuum tube is not therefore a functional concept. "Playing a role in voltage regulation" would have to enter into its W-definition; otherwise all concepts used to refer would be functional. It may be the case that a part or process of an organism is wonderfully adapted for the performance of a function, but even if the part or process were designed by God or by an entelechy for

---

[5] It is assumed that s' would still be s' minus s, i.e., that s' is so defined that s is no necessary part of it, and that the same may be said, *mutatis mutandis*, for s and the environment.

the sake of the performance, the concept of the part or process
would not necessarily be a functional concept.

Many concepts employed by the biologist are clearly functional;
others, while not obviously functional, can be shown to be so by an
examination of their use. Among obviously functional concepts I
would count "kidney," "gonad," "lung"—in short, most, though not
all, organs; "male," "female," "gamete," "symbiote," "cryptic" and
"warning coloration"; in ethology, as might be expected, the names
of responses and "releasers" [6] are often functional: consider "escape," "attack," "sexual display," "danger signal," "threat," "fanning"
(of an egg clutch), etc. The fundamental concepts of "organ," "analogy," "metabolism," and "adaptation" represent special cases: they
are not functional with respect to a previously specified F', but to
say, for example, that x is an organ, or x is adaptive, is to say that
there exists some F' to which x contributes.

ARE THERE SPECIFICALLY BIOLOGICAL CONCEPTS?

The claim that biology does and should employ "specifically biological" concepts, and the significance of that claim, may be assessed
with the aid of the foregoing distinctions. Two questions need to be
answered: To what uses may polytypic, historical, and functional
concepts be put? and, Do these three types of concepts provide us
with a means of describing a class of "specifically biological" concepts?

There can be no doubt that concepts of these types are useful,
since biologists do in fact use them, and there can be no doubt that
no physical scientist would feel satisfied with any physical theory
that employs them. From the point of view of a fully systematic and
well formalized theory such as Newtonian mechanics, such concepts
quite rightly appear to be so much excess baggage, irrelevant to the
theory proper, or at best, temporary stopgaps. This can be seen by
considering a logical feature that polytypic, historical, and functional concepts have in common, namely, that in order to apply
them truly to any system s, certain facts must be true about systems
other than s: some of the properties of s must be widely distributed
in a class of systems that may bear absolutely no relevant causal

---

[6] Tinbergen, *Study of Instinct,* pp. 55–56.

relations to s; or certain events, the "P-events," must have occurred in the past; or s must contribute to a function F' of a distinct system s' when s' is in some environment. To use a suggestive, although regrettably unclear term, concepts of this type signify *extrinsic* properties of a system. They relate s to external events or systems that may have no causal influence upon s, and the concepts can (logically) be applied to the system only if these relations in fact obtain. Evidently, when s is an isolated system, if we can describe its behavior, we do not need for its description a concept that explicitly relates it to other systems;[7] concepts of other types always could be found for the description of s.

What, then, are the biological uses of these concepts? Let us take a closer look at the descriptive or narrative uses of historical concepts. Suppose a physicist says, "By an A-alpha particle, I shall understand alpha particles yielded by radioactive decay; all others I will call B-alpha particles." The physicist could certainly utilize these concepts, e.g., in describing an experimental setup ("Rutherford directed A-alpha particles toward . . ."); or in writing a safety manual ("One should be especially careful of A-alpha particles since their energy . . ."); and so on. But unless the two types of particles showed differences in behavior, the concepts would not be used in a theory, and if they did show differences, the differences, and not the origin, would be made the basis of a W-definition of the concepts. In a sense, historical concepts seem to embody the genetic fallacy.

This is of course a contrived and highly simplified example, but the point to note is that its simplicity strikes us—we see the absurdity of the concept "A-alpha particle"—because the distinction is made within a familiar theory which tells us that differences in the behavior of alpha particles are, in all probability, conveniently explicable in terms of mass, energy, etc. Now suppose that a biologist says, "By a haploid organism I mean any organism whose body cell(s) contain n/2 chromosomes when its parents' body cells contain n (when n is even), or $n/2 \pm \cdot 5$ (when n is odd)." This does not, I trust, strike us as absurd, although, from the point of view of the logic of this W-definition, it is on a par with the W-definition of "A-alpha particle." This indicates that the difference lies not in the

[7] To be sure, the laws we employ are assumed to hold for classes of systems.

logic of definition but in the theoretical context in which the definition is constructed.

The things that can be done with the concept of a haploid organism are by no means trivial. It can be used in natural historical description, e.g., "Parthenogenetic offspring are often haploid"; "When
organisms show an alternation of generations, there is alternation
between haploid and diploid organisms" (this might be regarded as
a law); and so on. In addition, the concept can be used in the
W-definition of series of distinct concepts, e.g., "haploid cell," "haploid number," "polyploid," etc. The introduction of the historical
concept does not strike us as absurd, and is not absurd (nor restricted to narrative uses) because there is no theory that would
allow us to formulate conveniently and accurately the relations of
haploid organisms to other organisms in terms of concepts that are
not historical. We utilize the fact that an organism is haploid to
formulate (and explain) relations that hold, no doubt, only because
all and only haploid organisms have certain "intrinsic" properties.
The difficulty, of course, lies in the fact that we do not know what
they are, or even though we have some idea of what they are, our
theory is inadequate to locate them in the particular organism.

For the present, let this single example serve as the paradigm of
a theoretical use for an "extrinsic" concept. Examples of other functions for historical concepts, and for polytypic and functional concepts as well, will be multiplied in the sequel. We shall now turn
to the second question—the question with which the chapter began,
viz., what are the features of "distinctively biological" concepts?

Any concept deserves this title (of praise, for the organismic
biologist) if it meets the following conditions:

1) It is biological in subject matter. This is not very definite,
but in most cases there would be little room for misunderstanding.
"Cell," "gamete," etc., qualify; "lever," "electron," etc., do not; there
could be some doubt about "insulin," "photosynthesis," "respiration,"
i.e., those concepts which in fact apply only to organic systems,
but which are definable in terms that are universally agreed to belong to physics and chemistry proper. The borderline cases will not
however, at least for the most part, concern us here.

2) The mode of definition of the concept is of a type not, or sel-

dom, employed in physics and chemistry. By a mode of definition I understand, e.g., polytypic E-definition in terms of physical properties of a concept that is historical (or functional) in W-definition; W-definition by reference to historical antecedents; and so on.

3) The function of the concept is to provide the biologist with a "key position" for the analysis of phenomena that depend upon the organization of physical, chemical, or higher level parts, without taking explicit account of the parts, their organization relations, and the laws that describe their interactions. This is one function of specifically biological concepts as the term is understood by organismic biologists, and it is the function, as I see it, of the concepts that answer to condition 2).

CHAPTER III

Models in
Biological Theory

In the sense in which the term will be understood in this study, models serve a number of essential and pervasive logical roles in biological theory, and indeed in all the sciences. What these roles are and what are the general features of models in virtue of which they qualify for them constitute the problems of the present chapter. I shall first distinguish various senses of the term 'model,' and explain the sense in which I am using the term, utilizing a rather detailed account of a particular model (borrowed from Rashevsky) as a paradigm case. The theoretical functions of a model will be stated, and the techniques for realizing them will be analyzed. It will be maintained that models have logical, and not merely psychological uses, and that models in fact serve most of the functions commonly assigned to theories.

All this may seem to be a heavy load for a concept as thin and limited in applicability as the concept of a model, for writers on this subject have commonly assigned to models the logically modest, if psychologically necessary, functions of aiding scientists in picturing phenomena by means of familiar concepts and suggesting further lines of research, by way of analogy, that might otherwise be overlooked. Explanatory power is thus tacitly denied the model and localized in the theory. This view is supported by numerous studies in the logic of explanation, which have identified *an* explanation with a class of propositions meeting certain formal and material conditions. If the theory is distinguished from the model, and if the theory itself is conceived as a set of propositions, the natural further step of identifying explanations with a class of propositions drawn partly from the theory and, in some cases, from the empirical protocol completes the process of restricting the possible functions of models.[1]

I do not intend to question in any way the psychological and heuristic value of models, but I think that too exclusive attention to this aspect of their use has led to an undervaluing of their other uses, in the case of some types of models, that is tantamount to misrepresentation. I shall, then, emphasize the explanatory role of models, and indicate the respects in which the theory of models as heuristically useful analogies misrepresents this role.

TYPES OF MODELS

The term 'model' is used by philosophers of science in at least four distinct senses, and each sense stands in need of some clarification.

1. "Model" sometimes means "interpretation of a calculus." This includes the case in which an axiomatic system is given an interpretation for the sake, e.g., of proving the axioms consistent or independent; and the case in which the higher level terms of the calculus for an empirical theory are assigned meanings outside the theory. The latter case, in which we have a "model for a theory," is discussed by Braithwaite.[2] This is of course a legitimate sense of the term, and it must be admitted that such models are used and are useful both in logical theory and empirical science. Misunderstanding is likely to arise, however, if we interpret the views of writers such as Braithwaite as an effort to explicate the concept "model" in all its uses, as their language sometimes suggests.[3]

2. Some specialized mathematical techniques for analyzing and selecting empirical data are known as "models." Or, since in the discussion of these techniques it is not customary to identify the model with either the technique of treatment, the mathematical method, or the selection of the data, perhaps we should say noncommittally that

---

[1] In a view such as Braithwaite's, the model possesses all the explanatory power of the theory, since both are considered as alternative interpretations of the same calculus. Nevertheless, the model is logically superfluous. Braithwaite, *Scientific Explanation*, pp. 90, 92.

[2] *Ibid.*, pp. 88–96.

[3] Braithwaite sometimes drops the qualifying phrase "for a theory," and speaks merely of "models." *Ibid.;* cf. Toulmin, *Philosophy of Science*, pp. 12, 35.

we have an instance of the use of a model when experiments are performed and the data analyzed by means of the application of certain
special mathematical methods. These models are usually termed
"mathematical models" (other models also receive this title, however); examples are multiple factor, latent structure, and scalogram
analysis, and the application of the theory of games to problems
in economic theory. I shall not be concerned with models in this
sense, although developments in evolution theory initiated by Sir
R. A. Fisher's classical work,[4] which I shall consider, have been
termed "mathematical models." These developments, I believe, are
indeed a case of model building, but in another sense; it is merely
accidental that these models also utilize the special mathematical
methods of population genetics. One does not call Faraday's force
line model a mathematical model simply because mathematical
equations figure in electromagnetic theory.

3. The term 'model' is sometimes used literally to mean "replica."
Rosenblueth and Wiener use the term 'material model' in this sense,
and define it as follows: "A material model is the representation of
a complex system by a system which is assumed simpler and which
is also assumed to have some properties similar to those selected for
study in the original complex system."[5] The replica may be either
natural or man-made. If we have two systems that are similar with
respect to some "structural properties," and dissimilar in other
respects, the one is a model of the other if it is either simpler or
more convenient to work with, for this or any other reason.[6] The
difference between the model and the more complex system (called
its "field") that makes the model useful may be a reduction in
number of parts, with maintenance of only a few common morphological properties, as in the gelatin-cup models that exhibit gastrula-
tion; or the relevant difference may be only a difference of spatial
and temporal scale. This consideration leads these authors to the
unorthodox terminological position that a rat may be a model of a
large mammal, and that a population of fast-breeding animals may
be a model of a slower breeding population.[7]

---

[4] Fisher, *Genetical Theory.*
[5] Rosenblueth and Wiener, "Role of Models," *Philosophy of Science,* XII, 317.
[6] *Ibid.,* pp. 317–18.   [7] *Ibid.,* p. 320.

The term 'model' is of course legitimately used in the phrases 'model for a theory,' 'mathematical model,' and 'material model.' There are indeed such models, and it is well to investigate them thoroughly. Much of the current discussion of models, while not employing this three-way distinction and hence not explicitly restricted to one or another of these types of models, is nevertheless germane only to one of them. When methodologists of the social sciences speak of models, they are usually concerned with the second type. "General" methodologists such as Braithwaite and Toulmin seem to be concerned with the first type. Braithwaite does use the term 'model for a theory,' but he does not contrast it with other senses. The failure to observe these distinctions, or analogous ones, has resulted in some confusion; it has obscured the fact that the limitations and dangers inherent in the use of mathematical models are different from those encountered in the use of models for theories. Moreover, it has encouraged a considerable amount of somewhat loose and offhand reference to models, encouraging undue confusion between theories and models.[8] As a result, the concept of a model has become very vague. In fact, it is a kind of residual grab bag into which the nonlogical activities of science are indiscriminately thrown.

4. The three types of models distinguished do not represent an exhaustive classification. On the contrary, there is one type of model that seems to me of preeminent interest, which is profitably placed in a distinct category.[9] It is this fourth type that will concern us in the present study; I will subsequently mark it by means of the bare unqualified term 'model.' An explicit definition will be deferred until the concepts that will be utilized in the definition have been introduced and illustrated.

Examples of models in this fourth sense are easily found. They include the well-known biophysical models of cell-division, gastru-

[8] The description of a model given by Altschul and Biser is a complete description of a theory, except that they exclude general hypotheses. Altschul and Biser, "Unique Mathematical Models," *Philosophy of Science*, XV, 13–14.
[9] Even the resulting classification still is not exhaustive, especially if we include the philosophical senses of the term 'model.' For example, Wittgenstein's language games, Newton's equations of motion, and the subject-predicate propositional forms are often called models.

lation, mitosis, etc.; the evolutionary models associated with the
names of Fisher, J. B. S. Haldane, E. B. Ford, and Sewall Wright;
the neural models of W. McCulloch, W. Pitts, N. Rashevsky, and
A. S. Householder; and the "feed-back" models of W. R. Ashby
and the cyberneticists. An analysis of the reasons why all these cases
are termed models, and a discrimination of their essential elements,
reveals a type of model, I shall maintain, that represents one of the
most widespread and fruitful of the theoretical gambits available
to empirical science. To this end, I shall investigate one such model
—the construction of a neural network for the purpose of explaining a psychophysical law—and generalize the results over a much
wider range of models. The chosen paradigmatic model has two
chief advantages: it is an instance of an analysis that would be accepted unanimously as a model; and it is admirably clear and simple. If we take seriously the reasons for regarding this paradigm
as a model, we are obliged to see in model construction a tool whose
power has perhaps not been sufficiently appreciated.

Some of the models that I have mentioned as examples of the
fourth category have been regarded as models of a theory or as
mathematical models. I will present reasons for regarding this as
a confusion and for treating them *sui generis* as suggested. Proof
will have to wait for the analysis of the concept of a model and its
illustration in the paradigm.

A WORKING EXAMPLE OF A MODEL

The model that will serve as my working example is a particular
application of a type of model that has been developed for relating
the results of neurological research to more general problems of
animal behavior. Its details are taken from N. Rashevsky. What follows is a close adaption of his treatment.[10]

The law to be explained is a simplified statement of human
psychophysics (hereafter called "L_m"): "If a cold object is held to
the skin for a moment and removed, a sensation of heat will be felt;
if it is applied for a longer time, the sensation will be only of cold,
with no preliminary warmth at all."[11] The problem is to construct
a neural network that will show properties easily correlated with
the occurrences described in the law. For this purpose, a number of

[10] Rashevsky, *Mathematical Biophysics*, pp. 539–42.   [11] *Ibid.*, p. 540.

presuppositions are necessary. In addition to the usual all-or-nothing principle of neural activation, we need the following:

1) Cold activates certain receptors, heat others
2) A sensation of warmth is felt if certain neurons (not receptors) are activated; a sensation of cold, if others are activated
3) The time of transmission of a neural impulse along an axon is very small, and may be neglected
4) The time delay of transmission across a synapse is strictly constant, and the same for all synapses
5) Inhibition of a neuron by an inhibiting fiber is total
6) A neuron, other than a receptor, is activated only if it synapses with at least two activated terminal bulbs of one or more other neurons

In order to construct the simplest net that will explain the psychophysical law, Rashevsky lets N_1 and N_2 represent, respectively, heat and cold receptors, and N_3 and N_4 represent neurons whose activity is attended, respectively, by sensations of heat and cold. Assuming that the cold object is touched to the skin for a time less than the unit of the synaptic delay, and letting "$N_i(t)$" mean "N_i fires at t" (where the unit of time is the synaptic delay), the law can then be described in the notation of Boolean algebra:

$$N_3(t) \equiv N_1(t-1) \vee (N_2(t-3) \times \overline{N_2(t-2)})$$
$$N_4(t) \equiv N_2(t-2) \times N_2(t-1)$$

The final net exhibiting these properties is shown below. Loops are inhibiting fibers, and dots are terminal bulbs.

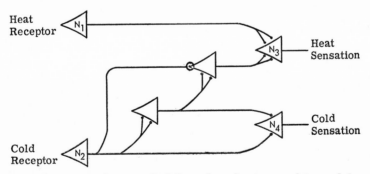

From the point of view of philosophy of science, this model presents a number of interesting problems. It is "interlevel"; it takes account of "organization"; and it embodies a number of specialized assumptions made for the purpose of simplification. To facilitate the discussion of these problems, a number of technical distinctions will now be introduced.

Following Rosenblueth and Wiener, I shall term the phenomena to be explained, and the systems exhibiting the phenomena, the "field" of the model. It is desirable, however, to distinguish the field itself from the systems whose properties are invoked in explanation of the field. These systems and the phenomena they exhibit, I call the "subject" of the model. In the typical case, the subject systems are physical parts of the field. The known properties of the subject systems utilized in the model may be called the "primary subject descriptions." In general, these descriptions are law-like statements. It is important to notice that the distinction between the *field* and the *subject* of a model is not the same distinction that is commonly drawn, in one or another terminology, between the phenomenon and its model. The latter distinction seems to me more misleading than useful, since it inevitably leads the methodologist to the view that the task of the model-builder is to establish an "isomorphism" between the model and the phenomenon, and too often elicits such bits of wisdom as, "The model is not the thing." All this obscures the essential question, namely, how a model employs the known properties of parts of the system (or its environment) under consideration.

The various functions of models are included under the very broad and somewhat vague heading of "simplification." Scientists have recourse to model explanation when the phenomena under consideration present complexities that, for whatever reason, defy analysis adequate for explanatory purposes on the basis of the existing theory of the field. I distinguish two types of assumptions characteristic of models, both of which may serve the purpose, among others, of simplification.

1. *Subsidiary hypotheses.* These are law-like statements, usually about the model's subject, which are either known to be false, or else not known to be true. Under many circumstances, of course, the use of a hypothesis known to be false would be entirely inappropriate; it violates, for example, Hempel and Oppenheim's material

requirement that every proposition in the *explanans* of an explanation be true.[12] Nevertheless, for reasons to be discussed, this requirement may profitably be waived in model-explanations.

2. *Simplifying assumptions.* These are existential statements that postulate the existence of elements of the subject, or describe contingent, as against nomological, relations between these elements. If, for example, an engineer amused himself by working out a schematic diagram for the control circuit of an elevator, a description of the circuit components and their hookup would be existential statements in this sense. In the model, these statements are called "simplifying" because, among other things, they serve to reduce the structural complexity of the field; they are called "assumptions" because they are either known to be false, or are not known to be true. The distinction between simplifying assumptions and subsidiary hypotheses parallels the usual distinction between particular statements of the boundary conditions and the general nomological statements in an explanation. These distinctions now will be amplified, and utilized in the description of the functions and logical peculiarities of models.

THE FUNCTIONS OF MODELS

Models have many uses. In fact, I would regard a model as a part of a theory, and treat the special uses of models as special cases of the general role of theory. We may divide the functions of models into two categories, explanatory and nonexplanatory. I agree with the prevalent view that treats the latter functions as auxiliaries of the former, since it has been shown that prediction, control, "understanding," the discovery of causes—in short, the functions of science—are to be clarified through the theory of explanation. I do not agree, however, with the relegation of nonexplanatory functions to the category of "heuristic functions," if they are thereby dismissed by the philosopher on the ground that any questions that may arise concerning them fall into the province of psychology. The techniques of methodological analysis may and should be applied to them.

[12] Hempel and Oppenheim, "Logic of Explanation," in *Philosophy of Science*, ed. Feigl and Brodbeck, p. 322.

Briefly, the nonexplanatory functions I shall emphasize are the following:

Demonstration of a way to simplify a complex subject matter without naive oversimplification; and correlatively, indicating precisely what must be done to eliminate the simplification, if so desired

The development of techniques for applying theoretical concepts and principles of demonstrated fruitfulness in one region of science to a region where they have not been applied

The analysis of the adequacy for a given purpose of a set of theoretical concepts and principles; or, what is perhaps a restatement of this, the analysis of the adequacy of a "point of view"

The formulation of possible mechanisms underlying a phenomenon

The explanatory functions of models are exhausted by the explanation of hypotheses (laws) and of particular occurrences. (Classes of particular occurrences, or effects such as neoteny, hybrid vigor, etc., when not expressible as universal hypotheses, are explained exactly like particular occurrences.) Lest explanation be conceived too narrowly, it may be worth while to point out that among *explananda* in these two categories we commonly find not only hypotheses like Mendel's laws, and events such as a particular case of regeneration, but also orders of events in a temporal sequence, sizes, shapes, geographical distributions, etc. *Explananda* like these are common in all the sciences. No special problem is raised in explaining them except in so far as their explanations are genetic or teleological.

We shall consider first the explanatory functions of models, and then their nonexplanatory functions.

The field of Rashevsky's neural net model is the particular psychophysical law L_m, but the model is presented by him merely as an illustration of a family of possible models, that may be applied to any psychophysical phenomena and in general to all animal behavior that we have reason to believe is integrated by a nervous system. How we draw the boundaries of the field of a given model, therefore, is somewhat arbitrary. A good model is often a member of a family whose members resemble one another in the possession of many common simplifying assumptions and subsidiary hypotheses, and differ from one another by the elimination or addition of one or several hypotheses or assumptions. In speaking of a model, confusion between the family and individual instances of the family can be avoided by specifying the field.

The field of a model is of course the source of *explananda* for the model. The logic of model-explanation of previously established laws of the field, or of particular occurrences falling under the scope of a law, is exactly parallel to the logic of explanation as formulated in the studies mentioned of Hempel and Oppenheim and Braithwaite. A law is said to be explained when it is deducible from the set of simplifying assumptions and subsidiary hypotheses, together with a set of primary subject laws; the particular occurrence is deducible by the addition to these sets of a class of particular statements specifying initial and perhaps further boundary conditions. Model-explanation of laws and occurrences is accordingly a special case of this more general explanatory pattern. (For the sake of brevity, I shall subsequently speak of this pattern as the Humean Pattern, since it is the conception of scientific explanation that emerges when Hume's analysis of causation is coupled with a distinction between description and explanation.)

There are, however, four important points to notice about model-explanation of laws.

1. Hempel and Oppenheim require that the *explanans* be true in order that we may truly say that the *explanandum* is explained. Braithwaite introduces a very similar requirement for the explanation of laws: it is necessary that the laws in the *explanans* be regarded as established.[13] In many models—in our paradigm, for example—some of the law-like statements are known to be false, and others cannot be regarded as established. Strictly speaking, then, these models are not explanations. They do, however, provide hypothetical explanations, in the sense that, if the subsidiary hypotheses and simplifying assumptions happened to be true, the *explanandum* would be explained. This property they share with genuine explanations, in virtue of their possession of all the logical

[13] Braithwaite, *Scientific Explanation*, p. 343.

conditions of adequacy of the Humean Pattern. Moreover, it must not be supposed that the point of these models is to offer a strict explanation of their ostensible *explananda*. The point of model-explanation is a large topic, to be examined shortly. At this time we need only indicate that, for example, Rashevsky offered his model as an illustration of a method. The fact that a model has the look of an explanation does not mean that its function is to explain, although this may indeed, in some cases, be one of its functions. I shall call any ostensible explanation that conforms to the Humean Pattern in every respect save the material requirement that the *explanans* be true, a "quasi-explanation."

2. In Braithwaite's formulation, a law is to be regarded as explained if it can be exhibited as a logical consequence of a set of higher level hypotheses which are themselves regarded as established.[14] As I understand him, hypothesis h_1 is said to be "higher level" with respect to h_2 if and only if h_1 entails h_2, with or without the help of other empirical statements, and if h_1 entails testable hypotheses other than h_2, with or without the help of other empirical statements. Thus the *explanandum* is always of lower level than the hypotheses in the *explanans*. There is no difficulty involved in this convention, but it can lead to a misunderstanding of the logical structure of some theories, *viz.*, those theories that explain the behavior of a system by reference to its microstructure.[15] For to say that h_1 is of a "higher level" than h_2 suggests that in a particular sense h_1 is more general than h_2. The sense of relative generality which the language of relative levels suggests, is relative generality with respect to a body of theory T. This concept may be briefly explicated as follows: Let T be a particular theory and let C be the class of descriptive concepts that occur in that theory. Then, if h_1 and h_2 are hypotheses of T, and H_1 and H_2 are the classes of conditions sufficient, respectively, for the exemplification of h_1 and h_2, and if only members of C are members of H_1 and H_2, then h_1 is "more general than" h_2 with respect to T if and only if H_2 is a proper subclass of H_1. Stated less formally, this means that

---

[14] *Ibid.*

[15] This convenient term is borrowed from Hempel and Oppenheim, "Logic of Explanation," in *Philosophy of Science*, ed. Feigl and Brodbeck, p. 332.

h_1 is more general than h_2 if both are hypotheses within a particular theory and if h_1 is exemplified under some conditions where h_2 is not exemplified, provided that the concepts in terms of which their scopes are specified are concepts from that same theory. The relative generality of two hypotheses is not defined if they are parts of two different theories, unless there is a third theory which includes them both. The significance of the provision that the scope of the hypotheses be described in terms of C lies in the fact that we should want to say that not the number of circumstances, but the number of kinds of circumstances under which the hypothesis is exemplified determines the degree of generality of the hypothesis. The notion of a kind of circumstances under which a hypothesis is exemplified can be given sufficient restriction (since a given kind can in general be divided into a number of kinds in an indefinitely large number of ways) only in reference to a concept already associated with the hypothesis in question. We would not, for example, in one sense of the word "general," hold that L_m, whose scope is specified in part by reference to taxonomic groups, is less general than the all-or-nothing principle whose scope is limited to neural elements, simply on the ground that there are as many kinds of neural elements as there are taxonomic groups characterized by a nervous system, and that not all such groups exemplify L_m. The taxonomic group-concepts are not part of the machinery of neurophysiology, as they are of animal psychology. Of course, if significant physiological differences were found between the neurons of different taxonomic groups, we would have the germ of a theory in reference to which the relative generality of these two hypotheses could be evaluated. Otherwise, they are not comparable.

In this sense of "more general," a higher level hypothesis in an *explanans* need not be more general than the *explanandum;* and very often, when the concepts and hypotheses of one theory are utilized in explaining the hypotheses of another theory by description of microstructure, the former hypotheses will not be more general (or indeed less general) than the latter. This distinction between "higher level" and "more general" is worth insisting upon in order to counteract the widely held, although largely implicit, view that explaining a law consists in the construction of a theoretical system in which the *explananda* appear as special cases, or as applications through a logical applicative principle, of more general hypotheses. L_m is surely not a special case of any neurophysiological law, nor are, e.g., the principles of evolution theory special cases of the principles of population genetics. One of the chief virtues of models consists in their providing the means for explaining the principles of a theory without constructing more general principles.[16]

3. In Rashevsky's model we have a case of interlevel explanation, in an altogether different sense of the term "level." The question of interlevel explanation has occupied a large part of the philosophizing about biological theory because it is acknowledged that biological phenomena represent the outcome of the organized activity of systems which themselves do not exhibit these phenomena, and whose description is the task of other natural sciences. All questions of "emergence" aside, it ought to be possible in principle, at least in many cases, to explain the phenomena shown by biological systems through reference to the physicochemical or other parts of the systems. Systems so explainable are said to be on a "higher level of organization" than the systems mentioned in the *explanans*. More precisely: suppose we have a system s_1 which exhibits the class of phenomena P_1; and that S_2 is the class of all the physical parts of s_1. Then the phenomena in P_1 are of a higher level of organization than the phenomena in P_2 whenever s_1 does not exhibit any of the phenomena in P_2; every member of S_2 exhibits at least one phenomenon in P_2; and no phenomenon in P_1 occurs unless each system in S_2 exhibits at least one phenomenon in P_2. Notice that the definition explicitly defines levels of organization for classes of phenomena, not classes of systems. The definition could easily be generalized, however: we may say that system s_1 possesses a higher level of organization with respect to P_1 and P_2 than the systems in S_2. Ordinarily, the so-called "problem of organization" arises when the concepts employed in the description of P_1 belong to a science not concerned with the description of P_2, and these concepts do not occur in the language developed for the description of P_2. The concept of "warm sensation" is no part of the language of neuro-

---

[16] Not all such explanations, however, are model-explanations.

physiology, and the concepts of "neuron," "terminal bulb," etc., would not ordinarily be considered part of the language of psychophysics.

In terms of this definition of "higher level of organization" we may define "interlevel explanation" as follows. We have an interlevel explanation of a phenomenon (hypothesis, occurrence) p_1 in terms of a class of phenomena P_2, where T_2 is the theory customarily employed in the description of P_2, if and only if:

1) It is possible to construct a logically and materially adequate explanation in the Humean Pattern whose *explanandum* is a description of p_1; and

2) Whose *explanans* is constructed exclusively out of (*a*) hypotheses and statements of initial and boundary conditions describing P_2, and employing only terms in T_2, and (*b*) universally quantified implications of the form 'A $\supset$ B,' where A is a matrix containing no terms that occur in the *explanandum*, and B is a matrix containing no terms that occur in T_2; and

3) p_1 and P_2 are on different levels of organization [17]

With the help of this definition, incidentally, we may define the expression "T_1 is reducible to T_2." Let T_1 be a theory that employs some theoretical terms that T_2 does not, and let T_2 be defined as above; then T_1 is reducible to T_2 if every phenomenon truly described in T_1 is subject to an interlevel explanation in terms of phenomena described by T_2.[18]

Model-explanations are not the only interlevel explanations, but it is evident, if only by an inspection of our example, that models are especially suited for interlevel explanations in the various biological sciences. The hierarchical organization of biological systems, from biocoenoses down to molecules, or their constituents, is a point emphasized by many writers, and especially by the organismic bi-

---

[17] The implications may be either "coordinating" definitions, in which case we could write the unnecessarily stronger biconditional; or they may be empirical hypotheses, e.g., in Rashevsky's model, the hypothesis connecting neural activity with sensations.

[18] This definition is a considerably modified and slightly weakened adaptation of a definition due to A. Tarski and J. H. Woodger. Woodger, *Biology and Language*, pp. 271–72. Also, it seems to me equivalent in intent and outcome to a definition offered by Nagel, "Mechanistic Explanation," *Philosophy and Phenomenological Research*, XI, 330.

ologists. If the systems on the higher levels of the hierarchy exhibit phenomena which the constituent systems do not, we clearly
have a case of different levels of organization corresponding to the
levels of the hierarchy, and one of the conditions of interlevel explanation is realized. Model-explanation is then needed if any of
the following epistemological conditions are met:

1) The causal relations between s_2 systems—the parts of s_1—are
   inadequately described; this corresponds to the absence of
   the much discussed "composition rules" governing the interaction of complexes [19]

2) It is impossible in practice to apply the laws of the s_2 systems,
   either (a) because the requisite initial and boundary conditions are unknown,[20] or (b) because the available deductive
   apparatus for deriving the *explanandum* is too weak

3) The requisite conditionals of the form 'A ⊃ B'—the coordinating definitions, or "transordinal" laws [21]—may be missing

The two levels of phenomena related in the interlevel explanation correspond to the field and the subject of the model; and the
difficulties represented by these three epistemological conditions
are not insuperable in the sense that, without eliminating them,
quasi-explanations can be constructed by the choice of suitable simplifying assumptions and subsidiary hypotheses.

4. Rashevsky points out that there are two different approaches
to the theory of the central nervous system. One is able to

postulate a few mathematically definite laws of interaction between two
adjacent neuroelements and then to consider to what consequences such
laws of interaction lead when applied to different geometrical arrangements of the interacting elements. In other words, the attempt [can be]
made to reduce the tremendous complexity of functions of the central

[19] For example, Broad, *The Mind,* pp. 61–81; and Madden, "Science in
Gestalt Theory," in *Philosophy of Science,* ed. Feigl and Brodbeck, pp. 566–
68.

[20] In biology sheer numbers of parts that must be distinguished constitute a
major barrier not only to the discovery of laws describing their interaction,
but also to the application of those laws that are discovered. The law, e.g., for
rate of diffusion of a fluid through membranes is known, but an attempt to
apply the law to the problem of organizer activity in morphogenesis is
practically excluded by the number and kinds and variability of the membranes the organizer must pass.

[21] The term is used by Broad, *The Mind,* p. 79.

nervous system to the complexity of its structure, keeping the fundamental dynamic processes as simple as possible. A different line of approach is also possible, namely, to consider theoretically the structure of
the central nervous system, with its tremendous number of neuroelements, as quasi-homogeneous and to try to account for the enormous
complexity of its functions as postulating correspondingly complex dynami-
cal laws of interaction between the individual elements.[22]

The former of these approaches well exemplifies an important
class of essays at model building. The temptation to assimilate complexity of function—not only in the sense of range of classes of
phenomena exhibited by a system such as a brain under various
conditions, but also the complexity of form of individual hypotheses—to complexity of structure seems justified on methodological
grounds. Moreover, the success of this approach is well attested
by the example of chemistry. Where internal structure is "tremen-
dously complex," as it is in most biological systems at the cell-level
and above, models are preeminently useful.

This is not to say that the second approach mentioned by
Rashevsky is not susceptible to model-treatment. The various
"molar" models of central nervous action exemplify this approach.[23]
I wish merely to emphasize at this point the unique value of model
methods of interlevel explanation under the joint circumstances of
structural and functional complexity.

NONEXPLANATORY FUNCTIONS OF MODELS

We shall now consider in turn the four nonexplanatory logical
functions of models enumerated on page 40.

SIMPLIFICATION OF COMPLEX SUBJECT MATTER. I agree with the
view that the features of models peculiar to them are the result of
their role in effecting simplification.[24] But there is a crucial distinction between simplification and oversimplification that must be
emphasized. A problem is simplified only if assumptions and hypotheses known to be false or not known to be true are introduced

---

[22] Rashevsky, *Mathematical Biophysics*, p. 355.
[23] For a summary treatment, see Morgan, *Physiological Psychology*, pp.
518–25.
[24] For a similar view, see Rosenblueth and Wiener, "Role of Models,"
Philosophy of Science, XII, 316; and Altschul and Biser, "Unique Mathematical Models," *Philosophy of Science*, XV, 13.

in such a way that provision is made for discounting or eliminating the resulting distortion. The technique of idealization so widespread in theoretical physics is an excellent example, although a special one, of simplification without oversimplification. It consists in treating a function of several arguments as a function of some subclass of the arguments, on the assumption that the remaining arguments are either constant, or make a negligible contribution to the value of the function. Thus provision is made for accounting for unforeseen results.

The techniques of simplification in model building include idealization as one gambit among many. We may distinguish the following important cases.

(a) *Simplifications introduced by way of the simplifying assumptions.* In Rashevsky's model, these are embodied in the choice of exactly six neuroelements in the construction of the net, and in the postulated interconnections among them. All such existential assumptions are in general eliminable; since they refer to the physical constitution of the model's subject, further investigation of a purely morphological type is theoretically sufficient for their elimination. If existential assumptions refer to unobservables, then we are no longer dealing with a model in my sense, but with a model for a theory in Braithwaite's sense.

It should be emphasized that simplifying assumptions may be introduced for a quite different purpose, namely, to provide for a system that will exemplify the boundary conditions necessary for the application of a primary subject law. In other words, a "mechanism" may be postulated.

The typical simplifying assumption consists in the reduction of the number of subject systems (parts) considered, or in the precise specification of the number of such systems. Examples are the model-explanation of human skin color in terms of a system of five multiple alleles; explanations of evolutionary change on the assumption that the population number is of a certain order of magnitude, such as the reciprocal of a selection coefficient; and all neural net models. Often a simplifying assumption asserts the presence of a system of a certain kind not known, on independent evidence, to be present.

(*b*) *Simplifications introduced by way of the subsidiary hypotheses.* These are of the essence of model technique. The six presuppositions of the nerve-net model (page 37) are all subsidiary hypotheses, with the possible exception of the first. In this model, these hypotheses, or others equally arbitrary, are necessary in the sense that they make possible the application of the Boolean algebra. But the use of the Boolean algebra is not arbitrary; it is based on an all-important property of the subject systems, namely, the all-or-nothing law of neural transmission. The hypotheses introduced here, as in every model, are in part controlled by the nature of the field, and in part by the known properties of the model's subject. This is the reason why it is so misleading to view a model as an analogy. Some models are accidentally of heuristic value only because the primary subject descriptions are more familiar, and perhaps more "picturable" than the field phenomena.

Among subsidiary hypotheses that effect some simplification, we may notice these cases. A primary subject hypothesis may be introduced in an idealized form; hypotheses 3), 4), 5), and 6) of the paradigm are of this type. Or known exceptions to subject hypotheses may be neglected; e.g., in many genetic models the facts of linkage and crossover are neglected. Such simplifications are sometimes eliminated by restricting the scope of application of the model itself; or, without narrowing the scope of the model, the simplifications may be shown to be innocuous by proving that the *explanandum* is deducible from the model with a high degree of probability. The latter is a widespread procedure in models whose subject laws are statistical, and when the *explanandum* is not fully or precisely quantified, e.g., in model estimation of evolutionary rates.

THE EXTENSION OF WELL-ESTABLISHED THEORY. If the point of model-building were to provide strict explanations, the false assumptions embodied in them would seem very odd indeed. But this is not their primary function, although many models are hazarded in the hope that the assumptions made are true. The development of a model which embodies only quasi-explanation is one aspect of the general scientific procedure of applying well-established and well-understood principles as widely as possible. The data, techniques, hypotheses, and concepts that have been developed by workers in a more or less closely restricted region are confronted with those of workers in other areas with the help of the mediating offices of the model. Most models cut across conventional disciplinary boundaries. R. Goldschmidt's famous chemical model of sex determination in the Gypsy moth; [25] the application of quantum theory and of thermodynamics to the problems of genetic continuity and mutation by Schroedinger [26] and Blum; [27] the use of the principles of catalysis, autocatalysis, and of the chemistry of colloids in models of plant growth, cell division, gene reproduction, the origin of life, and the development of polarity in the zygote are good examples of such interdisciplinary models.

The casting of models in the form of quasi-explanations is a device for demonstrating that the principles and concepts from one region of science possess the formal interrelations requisite for strict explanations in other regions. A particular model quasi-explanation is to be evaluated, then, not by reference to its success in the ostensible task of explaining the field to which it is actually applied, but in its power to generate a family of models which are capable of bringing successively larger bodies of established theory into relation with ever larger fields. The success of the model in this task is largely dependent upon the types of simplification it embodies, the ease of removal of these simplifications, and whether or not the simplifications are adapted for analogous applications to phenomena related to the original field. Rashevsky's model seems to be very strong in this respect. It quasi-explains only L_m, but simplifications of the type employed are easily removed (e.g., the assumption of a constant synaptic delay may be relaxed, since there are mathematical techniques for dealing with the resulting complications); and these and similar assumptions are applicable, and have been applied, to other hypotheses like L_m, to the analysis of neural inhibition itself, to various problems of conditioning and learning, etc.

THE EVALUATION OF A THEORETICAL "POINT OF VIEW." The remaining two functions of models are subordinate to the above two in the sense that simplification and the use of established principles and

[25] Goldschmidt, *Basis of Evolution*, pp. 234–37.
[26] Schroedinger, *What Is Life?*
[27] Blum, *Arrow and Evolution*, pp. 147–48.

concepts in the description of the model's subject are the features that enable models to perform the remaining functions. Of special interest in biological theory is the use of models in evaluating a theoretical approach to a subject matter—what biologists often call a "point of view." For example, the merits of a tropism or "forced movement" theory of animal behavior have often been discussed as if the question were to be settled by an appeal to a priori principles of methodology, but in practice both defenders and critics of the view point to the models of animal behavior that have been developed, the defenders with pride, the detractors with scorn. The early claims for the general applicability of tropism models have been restricted largely because of the inability of the models to be modified in ways appropriate for yielding quasi-explanations of relevant phenomena. The failure of vitalism was due finally to its inability to generate model-explanations. Nowadays the generality of neo-Darwinian selection theory is examined through an investigation of the relative merits of Darwinian and other models in accounting for phenomena such as aristogenesis, periods of explosive adaptive radiation, and crucial gaps in the fossil record.

This function of models is of course only a special case of the evaluation of a theory in terms of its fruits. It is worth noting, however, because of the special form such evaluation takes: the concepts and principles employed in description of the model's subject are not called into question, but only their adaptability to a new field. To investigate adaptability, one needs to attend closely to the amount and type of distortion (simplification) entailed by the actual adaptation.

THE FORMULATION OF POSSIBLE "MECHANISMS." The construction of a model always involves the postulation of a possible "mechanism" underlying the phenomena of its field. Indeed, the term "mechanism" refers in the broadest sense to a system of parts causally related to one another. More narrowly, the scientist often has reason to suspect that occurrences of a particular type ("effects") do happen; or he may wish to postulate the occurrence of an effect for the sake of explaining a different occurrence whose sufficient conditions are unknown. Under either of these circumstances, the construction of a model may serve to show that the occurrence or effect is possible, i.e., compatible with the known facts and hypotheses about the system in question. It may, for instance, be suspected that a major animal group such as the insects or vertebrates are immediate descendants of representatives of very dissimilar groups, e.g., the myriapods, or echinoderms. Prima facie, there might seem to be no way of deciding whether or not these transitions represent genuine evolutionary possibilities. The question can be approached through the construction of models of the problematical transition. Consider such a model for the derivation of the vertebrates from ancestral echinoderms: it is assumed that echinoderms possess a complement of genes that exhibit their effects primarily in the larval stage of development, adapting the organism to a way of life quite different from that of the adult; that the complement of genes that control metamorphosis may fail to exert their effect, but that the larvae may nevertheless reach sexual maturity. If this series of events were to occur, a population of reproducing organisms might result that in all relevant respects represents a new species: the population evolves, and gradually loses or modifies the genes that originally brought about metamorphosis, giving rise eventually to a primitive chordate.

This is merely the sketch of a model. A great deal of attention would have to be given to a comparison of chordates (or their larvae) to the larvae of echinoderms, and the model would finally receive little credence if no independent evidence for the possibility of the various steps could be found. In fact, such models have been widely accepted as offering explanations of the origin of various groups. Their function is to bridge the gap between groups which show great morphological divergence. Other models intended to reveal the possibility of suspected effects are Dobzhansky's model of the development of genetic isolation in populations briefly isolated by other factors;[28] the model of chance reduction of population variability;[29] Fisher's theory of the evolution of dominance;[30] and Simpson's explanation of hypertelic evolutionary trends.[31]

To summarize. A model is understood to be a technique of ex-

---

[28] Dobzhansky, *Genetics*, p. 256.   [29] *Ibid.*, pp. 127–29.
[30] Fisher, *Genetical Theory*, pp. 48–70, especially pp. 49–50.
[31] Simpson, *Major Features*, pp. 282–91.

plaining or quasi-explaining a class of phenomena (called the field) by reference to the properties of systems (called the subject), which are either parts of the system exhibiting the field phenomena or of its environment. The model introduces possibly or certainly false simplifying assumptions and/or subsidiary hypotheses for the sake of such explanations. The heuristic function of models has been minimized, and the logical function maximized; the view that properties of the organism cannot be explained by the use of models is rejected.[32] The function of models is ultimately to explain phenomena, but penultimately to approach the problem of organization by way of a simplified consideration of the organized parts; to confront the established results of one region of science with the unsolved problems of another; to serve in the analysis of the adequacy of a theoretical approach; and to demonstrate the compatibility of speculative hypotheses with the preestablished facts.

Models are devices for dealing with organization when it constitutes a problem. As such, one would expect organismic biologists to embrace model-building techniques with enthusiasm: Von Bertalanffy's movement in the direction of "General System Theory" is some evidence of sympathy.[33] On the other hand, model-building on the whole represents a "reductive" approach, and organismic biologists have in general been critical, e.g., of tropism models, chemical models in embryology, and even of the application of genetics to evolution theory. Enough has been said to indicate that such suspicion rests largely on a misunderstanding. For although most (but not all) models are interlevel, they need not refer to the systems studied professionally by physicists and chemists as the subject of models; model-building can and often does proceed entirely at the "biological" level. More fundamentally, the adverse view toward models overlooks the fact that distinctively biological concepts do not apply themselves miraculously, and that in point of fact the logical structure of theories in which these concepts are useful contains a significant model component. (A "theory" may be a family

[32] For an explicit statement of the view, see Mainx, *Foundations of Biology,* p. 27.
[33] Von Bertalanffy, *Problems of Life,* pp. 199–201; and Von Bertalanffy, "General System Theory," *British Journal for the Philosophy of Science,* I, 134–65.

of models—this point will be stressed in the chapter on selection theory.) I shall also subsequently discuss distinctively biological concepts with respect to their function of organizing data in a form amenable to model treatment, and both genetic and teleological explanation will be treated as subclasses of model-explanation.

CHAPTER IV

Systematics

In this chapter a detailed illustration of the utility in science of historical, functional, and polytypic concepts will be presented. This is, however, correlative with the larger purpose of interpreting an important methodological school within taxonomy. I try to show that these concepts are useful tools for describing the intent and practice of the New Systematics, and that the success of this school amply demonstrates the fruitfulness of concepts of these types.

THE LOGICAL CHARACTER OF A TAXONOMIC SYSTEM

It will be well to begin with an informal outline of the logical character of a taxonomic system, which, however, if axiomatized, would be sufficient for yielding formal proofs of the theorems needed in working with the system. The terminology introduced will be employed throughout the study.

A taxonomic system is a system of classes related in the following manner. A finite (and small) number of classes of classes, called taxonomic categories,[1] are enumerated and named, and arranged in serial order from 1 to n. The jth taxonomic category is said to be of *rank j*. The members of each category, called *taxa*, are classes of organisms. A taxon T which is a member of a category of rank j will be called a taxon of rank j (T_j). Every T_j ($j < n$) is included in a T_{j+1}; T_n is included in no taxon; no taxa are included in a T_1. The taxa of each rank are exclusive and exhaustive of the class of organisms, i.e., every organism is a member of one and only one taxon of each rank. Examples of taxonomic categories are "species," "genus," "phylum," etc. There is no general agreement on the num-

[1] I adopt the very useful distinction between taxonomic categories and taxonomic groups from Gregg, "Taxonomy," *American Naturalist*, LXXXIV, 430. For "taxonomic group" I shall use the term "taxon," suggested in a review by Parker-Rhodes, *Philosophical Review*, LXVI, 124.

ber of categories, and hence on the number of ranks, to be employed
in the systematic hierarchy. The number ranges in the neighborhood
of eighteen. This includes the standard categories from species to
kingdom, sub- and supercategories, the cohort, and the tribe. There
is universal agreement that the number of taxa of rank $j + 1$ should
be considerably smaller than the number of rank j. Examples of taxa
are "Homo sapiens," "Reptilia," "Diptera," etc. As Parker-Rhodes
remarks, this logical skeleton holds few surprises.[2] The surprises, if
they can be called such, are found when we come to consider how
the categories and taxa are defined.

The much discussed methodological problems of taxonomy cluster
about two fundamental questions: by what criteria are we to judge
what constitutes an adequate definition of the taxonomic categories
and of the taxa of the various ranks; and what significant natural
relationships between organisms do the taxa of the different ranks
reflect? For the taxonomist these are not bloodless academic questions, because the battles over both the details and the foundations
of the system have been and are being fought by protagonists with
only one foot firmly planted in the empirical materials; the other
foot is placed on the infirm ground of general questions of methodology, of which these two are the most discussed. Suppose, for instance, that the question of what rank in the hierarchy a certain
group occupies should arise. Should, e.g., the lagomorphs (hares
and conies) be assigned ordinal rank, or should they be included
within the order Rodentia? This can be answered only by an inspection of relevant facts about lagomorphs and rodents on the one
hand, e.g., how they compare anatomically, serologically, in distribution, etc., and by consideration of the high matters of policy that
dictate (or at least suggest) how the taxa of various ranks are to be
formed. It is fair to say that all the questions which have concerned
the writers on taxonomic methodology—the "reality" of species, the
status of the higher taxa (i.e., those of generic or higher rank), the
question of the basic taxonomic unit, the significance of morpholog-

[2] Parker-Rhodes, review of Gregg, *Philosophical Review*, LXVI, 124. His
own analysis of a taxonomic system is, however, surprising, since he makes the
relation between taxa of rank j and $j + 1$ one of membership rather than
inclusion.

ical as against "biological" taxon criteria—would vanish if only these two questions could be answered unequivocally.

A number of difficult problems stand in the way of such a straightforward solution, however. Most important, perhaps, is the fact that the taxonomic system is constructed for two distinct purposes.

1. *Classification*. The system must provide a catalogue, as complete and as convenient as possible, of all known organisms. The catalogue shall serve the purposes of ready identification, determinate reference, specimen pigeonholing, practical stratigraphy, etc. What is needed here is plainly a triangular hierarchy of the character outlined above, with each taxon circumscribed by reference to a property defined as the Boolean product of a set of characters of specimens. The set should be as small as practicable, and each character (the taxonomist's "diagnostic character") should above all be readily accessible without undue manipulation of the specimen, preferably to simple visual inspection or linear measurement. The character should be found in dead, preserved, and fairly young specimens, and should be present in the different types of polymorphic groups. The characters need have no adaptive or other biological significance. Emphasis upon this function of taxonomy, and upon the nature of taxa suggested by its pursuit, has determined the view that the systematist is like the library cataloguer, who works for the convenience of the researcher, but makes no substantive contributions to his researches. Taxonomy, W. M. Wheeler held, has no theory.[3]

2. *The Implementation of Theory*. The other function of taxonomy has been described by G. G. Simpson as follows: "Taxonomy in its various guises and branches eventually gathers together, utilizes, summarizes, and implements everything that is known about animals, whether morphological, physiological, psychological, or ecological."[4] Findings in every branch of biology may provide materials to direct the circumscription of taxa, and they are to be described in the manner which permits the highest degree of theo-

[3] Wheeler, "Biological Theory," in *Philosophical Biology*, ed. Wheeler, p. 192.
[4] Simpson, "Principles of Classification," *Bulletin of the American Museum of Natural History*, LXXXV, 1.

retical unification. This function has always been given a minimal recognition in the saying that taxa are natural kinds, and the taxonomic system a natural one, since its classificatory cuts lump together organisms with many attributes in common.

Before the advent of evolutionary theory, there was no way to state and justify a classificatory policy that reasonably could be expected to result in the greatest fruitfulness, but it was noticed as early at least as Aristotle that morphological diagnostic characters yielded a system more fruitful than classification by ecological properties. And it was discovered and accepted as an empirical fact that if a set of morphological diagnostic characters-in-common could be found for a given group, they were exceptionally reliable indices for a great many, indeed, a practically limitless, number of other morphological characters. After the adoption of the Linnaean system, it was further found that the morphological diagnostic characters of the taxa of species rank were good indices for ecological properties, as well as for the important property of fertility in matings within the taxon.

Evolution theory at once provided an explanation for these empirical facts and suggested a policy for implementing the formation of taxa that are likely to lead to the greatest number of predictions. This is to classify on the basis of phylogenetic descent, i.e., to place in the same taxa those organisms most closely related to each other. This has led to the adoption of the ideal of "monophyletic" classification, that no two distinct branches of a phylogenetic tree should lead into any one taxon. Taxonomy and evolution theory thus became inseparably intertwined. According to Julian Huxley, a leading spokesman for the New Systematics, as against the attitude of Wheeler, "the problem of systematics, regarded as a branch of general biology, is that of detecting evolution at work." [5]

THESES OF THE NEW SYSTEMATICS

The New Systematics has arisen in the attempt to adapt intractable empirical matter to the ideal of a classification based on phylogeny, which is at the same time useful as a catalogue. I shall outline

[5] Huxley, "Introductory," in *New Systematics*, ed. Huxley, p. 2.

the theses of the New Systematics which will be of concern to us.

The species is the taxon with the highest "degree of objectivity." It differs in kind from all other taxa.

The population, not the individual, is the basic taxonomic unit.

"Biological" criteria of species are to be employed; morphological taxonomic characters do not have special theoretical significance.

Wide use is to be made of quantitative techniques, especially of statistical methods.

THE SPECIES CONCEPT AND TAXA OF SPECIES RANK. We shall consider first the concepts of the species and those of the taxa of species rank. The analysis is not perfectly general since it is restricted to sexual organisms, but then, this restriction is implicit in the principles of the New Systematics.

It is often held that systematists employ two distinct concepts of the species. The neontologist's species concept is relatively simple, since he deals with species separated by gaps. The paleontologist, on the other hand, must deal with phyletic transformations of populations in time, and therefore any separation of the phyletic line into taxa of specific rank necessarily involves an arbitrary choice. These observations are true, but it does not follow that two distinct concepts of the species are involved. This belief rests on a confusion between well-defining and effectively defining a concept. As soon as this distinction is recognized, and it is acknowledged that "species" cannot be W-defined at all, the neontological and paleontological species concepts are seen to be the same.

That the species-category cannot be W-defined follows immediately from the generally acknowledged fact that no set of conditions is both necessary and sufficient for calling a group a species. This does not mean, however, that the decision to call a group a species is purely a matter of choice. There are *criteria of adequacy* for any W-definition of species, what I have called "W-defining criteria of adequacy." These criteria serve the double purpose of directing the formation of an E-definition and evaluating any tentative formulations. The criteria are:

1) Every member of a species T_s must be a member of a poten-

tially interbreeding hypothetical population comprised of all the members of T_s. Not all the members need be members of an actual natural population

2) Every member of a species T_s must be either a first-generation descendant of members of T_s, or else a first-generation descendant of members of a single population of potentially interbreeding organisms

The first criterion is the systematist's "biological" species-criterion; it expresses the view that the species is the *largest* taxon of interbreeding organisms. A certain vagueness should be noted, however, in the notion of "potentially interbreeding." It is not stated that any given male in T_s is a potential mate of every female in T_s. In the first place, it cannot hold for, e.g., sexless castes or abnormal individuals. These exceptions could be dealt with *ad hoc*, but I shall not take the time. In the second place, all that is intended is that any individual in T_s is a potential mate of an indefinitely large subclass of randomly selected members of T_s. This weakening of the criterion is made necessary by two situations that will be described below. It should be noticed that this criterion renders the species-concept "functional" in the sense defined. Although "species" is not W-defined, there is a "functional" criterion of adequacy for any W-definition. The function in question is self-reproduction: the taxonomic category "species" is applicable only to a group (the taxon of species rank) in which there exist systems (pairs of organisms) that contribute to the function of self-reproduction.

The second criterion renders the concept historical. It is a necessary supplement to the first for two reasons. It forbids inclusion in the same species phyletically distinct populations that might by chance be interfertile; and, most importantly, it provides the grounds for the introduction of evidence for species rank of any kind that might be shown, on the basis of any theory, to bear on the questions of phylogenetic origin. This, in a nutshell, is the reason for the relative devaluation of morphological species-criteria.

These two criteria are a reconstruction of the views and practice of the New Systematics. The criteria provide for the derivation of the E-definition of "species" that is actually employed. The E-definition is polytypic with respect to the G-class composed of the two criteria, and of any criteria derivable theoretically from the requirement of monophyletic descent.

It should be demonstrated that criteria 1) and 2) are necessary but not sufficient for placing a group at the species rank. This is easily demonstrated for the second: any taxon may be monophyletic in this sense. Would it not, however, be the case that the conjoint application of both is a sufficient condition? Two examples will show this is not the case.

Consider the following simplified case of evolution: a single genetically isolated population undergoes continuous change, but does not split into subpopulations. Suppose that the change continues for some millions of years; that the phenotypic differences accumulated in the long run are large; and that the genetic differences between distantly separated temporal slices of the population are sufficient to insure intersterility, if, *per impossibile,* the organisms at these slices were brought together. On the hypothesis, it is evident that any systematist would consider it desirable to split this phyletic line into a number of species, and perhaps even into a number of higher taxa. If the organisms at a given slice are interfertile with those at distantly neighboring slices in both time directions, there are a large number of pairs of slices that will include between them classes of interfertile forms. Since these classes are monophyletic, they would be entitled to species rank if the two criteria were regarded as jointly sufficient. But this would include each organism in the line in a large number of distinct species!

The temporal situation possesses a spatial analogue. An example is afforded by A. C. Kinsey's analysis of certain species-complexes in the gall wasp Cynips. These wasps are often found in long chains of local populations, each of which could freely interbreed with neighboring populations, but which cannot interbreed with more distant links in the chain. Chains of this type are known by systematists as "Rassenkreise" or "polytypic species." [6] If we assume that the whole chain is monophyletic, we would, on the assumption that free interbreeding is sufficient for species rank, classify every group of interfertile subpopulations as species. This again would include each

---

[6] The notion (and name) "polytypic class" was in fact suggested to me in considering the systematists' concept.

wasp in several species. And on the other hand, the systematist might wish to group a chain into a single species even though the ends of the chain are intersterile populations.

These situations suggest a way of treating the vagueness in the notion of "potentially interbreeding" a little more precisely. Consider one of Kinsey's Rassenkreise of eighty-six populations:[7] let f_1 be the property (of individual organisms) of being interfertile, in voluntary matings, with the members of population #1, and so on to f_{86}. The class of wasps in the Rassenkreis then form a fully polytypic class with respect to the G-class of all the f's. Each wasp possesses a large number of f's (in actuality, about eight); each wasp lacks about seventy-eight f's; and each f is possessed by large numbers of individuals (all those in any subclass of about eight populations). If we say that the Rassenkreis is polytypic with respect to interbreeding we may recast the first criterion by saying that every taxon of species rank must be at least polytypic with respect to interbreeding. The necessary arbitrary element of choice is maintained.

On the assumption that a group meets the W-defining species-criteria, it is possible to derive, by the application of a number of empirical principles, a test-procedure for determining with a high degree of probability whether or not a given group has these properties. The functional and historical criteria insure that every member of the group will share many genes in common. This is, of course, the theoretical justification for the search after morphological diagnostic characters-in-common applicable to individual specimens; and if the historical requirement is met, a number of inferences concerning the geographical distribution of the group are often warranted. It is impossible to infer that all the members of a monophyletic group will occupy geographically contiguous areas, but it is possible to infer that, under some conditions, a particular geographical distribution is highly unlikely on the assumption of monophyly. In other words, if we take into account geographical and geological data concerning land bridges, the climate at given periods, connections between bodies of water, etc., geographical contiguity may be weak evidence for, and lack of it strong evidence for, species status

---

[7] Wright, "Statistical Consequences," in *New Systematics*, ed. Huxley, p. 162.

in a group. Such evidence has to be evaluated in the light of other species-criteria.[8]

If a group shares many genes in common, the members will bear close morphological similarities to one another. These similarities are made the basis of the species-descriptions that occur in taxonomic journals. Every effort is made to strike a balance between the inclusion of too few and too many properties in a species-description. Too many are undesirable for reasons of economy; too few lead to ambiguity, since any given diagnostic character may be lacking in aberrant or fringe members of a species.

The other species-criteria—ethological, physiological, and the biological criterion of interfertility—are often lumped under the heading of "genetic" criteria.[9] And indeed they all constitute evidence of genetic similarity. Among these, the interfertility criterion is, from the point of view of the New Systematics, of the greatest importance. This is the reason why the criterion has been specified as a condition of adequacy for any species-definition. This importance is illustrated in the definition offered by Mayr: "Species are groups of actually (or potentially) interbreeding natural populations which are reproductively isolated from other such groups." [10] Dobzhansky, defining species from the point of view of one primarily concerned with distinguishing species from races or subspecies, proposes to "define species as that stage of evolutionary process, 'at which the once actually or potentially interbreeding array of forms becomes segregated in two or more separate arrays which are physiologically incapable of interbreeding.' " [11]

Suppose now we grant that the taxonomic category "species" cannot be W-defined, but is only subject to W-defining conditions of adequacy. Does it follow that the taxa of species rank cannot be W-defined? Is it not always possible to construct definitions of *Homo erectus, Felis leo,* etc., with the help of the various properties falling under the head of the morphological, physiological, etc., species-criteria, and to make these W-definitions by ruling that all and only

[8] Simpson, "Principles of Classification," *Bulletin of the American Museum of Natural History,* LXXXV, 7.
[9] Huxley, "Introductory," in *New Systematics,* ed. Huxley, p. 5.
[10] Mayr *et al., Methods and Principles,* p. 25.
[11] Dobzhansky, *Genetics,* p. 312.

those specimens which possess the properties mentioned are to
count as members of the species? It is certainly possible to define
classes (in the logician's sense) in this way, but, then, there is no
guarantee that a class so defined is a species. It can be a species only
if it does not violate the W-defining conditions of adequacy. And the
conditions laid down in a species-description bear only an empirical,
never a logical, relation to the conditions of adequacy. In view of
these facts, we may conclude that a definition by arbitrary fiat never
constitutes a W-definition of a taxon of species rank.

The real situation in taxonomy is not as black as this might lead
one to believe. We can construct E-definitions both of the species
category and of taxa of species rank. However, the E-definition of
the species category is polytypic with respect to the so-called
"species-criteria" of the New Systematics, and the E-definitions of
the various species are polytypic with respect to the class of "taxonomic characters."

The former point is explicitly supported by Julian Huxley:

There is no single criterion of species. Morphological difference; failure
to interbreed; infertility of offspring; ecological, geographical, or genetical
distinctness—all of those must be taken into account, but none of them
singly is decisive. Failure to interbreed or to produce fertile offspring is the
nearest approach to a positive criterion.[12]

Huxley's list could be expanded and refined, but his intent is plain.
He means that there is a group G of properties widely distributed
in the class of species; that each species has a number of these properties; and that no single property is possessed by each and every
species. On my definition, "species" is fully polytypic with respect
to G, and, in addition, is both a functional and historical concept.

With regard to the definition of taxa of species rank, I have already argued that ability to interbreed with other members of the
group and geographical contiguity are not decisive criteria for
ranking the group as a species. Application of the other species-
criteria to a particular group yields the taxonomic characters, among
which, it is hoped, will be found the morphological diagnostic
characters-in-common. For the sake of simplicity, we will show that
any species is polytypic with respect to the class of morphological

[12] Huxley, "Introductory," in *New Systematics*, ed. Huxley, p. 11.

taxonomic characters; exactly the same considerations allow us to generalize that class over ethological, physiological, etc., properties.

Among the class of morphological taxonomic characters of the type utilized in taxonomic descriptions, no one is sufficient for including a specimen in a given species. This statement cannot be strictly proved, since the number of such characters is limited only by the ingenuity of the taxonomist. But the consideration of the biological facts makes it very plausible, for suppose that all known members of a well-investigated species have property f, and that no other investigated organism has possessed f. Then, if a member of another species, even a closely related one, were to be discovered possessing f, this would in no case, of itself, be regarded as sufficient grounds for including the specimen in the original species. And a precisely analogous argument shows that no single morphological character is necessary for membership in a given species. But any acceptable taxonomic species-description does mention a number of characters that are widely distributed in the species, and perhaps even universally, and every specimen will possess a number of these characters. Of course, many species-descriptions to be found in the literature are not acceptable, and do not provide an E-definition of the species. But if a species is E-defined at all, it is polytypic with respect to the properties utilized in the description. If the species-concept is not fully polytypic, the description provides genuine diagnostic characters-in-common; but it should be noticed that the systematist never, or at any rate seldom, knows that his species-concept is not fully polytypic, and I suspect that many of the systematist's polymorphic species and Rassenkreise are.

The absence of W-definitions of the species category and of the various taxa of species rank is in part the cause and in part the effect of the polytypic character of species. Dobzhansky has insisted that a precise definition of the species category is in principle impossible, and would in fact cast doubt upon the doctrine of evolution.[13] A similar view was earlier upheld by G. C. Robson.[14] If a systematist is unwilling to stipulate a W-definition for the species category, and sticks by his resolution, he has committed himself to

[13] Dobzhansky, *Evolution*, p. 183.
[14] Robson, *Species Problem*, pp. 1–21.

polytypic taxa of species rank. On the other hand, the New Systematics is in part the outcome of the realization that species are in fact polytypic; a good part of the methodological literature of the New Systematics is devoted to the piecemeal destruction of various allegedly reliable species-criteria. Mayr, Linsley, and Usinger, for instance, point to the existence of morphologically very dissimilar conspecific forms, and to sympatric populations practically identical in morphology, but genetically intersterile.[15]

The ability to recognize that a group of organisms is polytypic presupposes at least a rough principle for segregating that group from other similar groups. All the New Systematists acknowledge such a principle in their insistence that the species category occupies a special place both in nature and in the systematic hierarchy. The attitude is stated by Huxley:

Species have a greater reality in nature, or, if we dislike the philosophical implications of this term, a greater degree of objectivity, than the higher taxonomic categories. . . . species are seen in the majority of cases to be definable as distinct, self-perpetuating units with an objective existence in nature, and therefore on a different theoretical footing from genera or families or other higher categories, which are not definable in this concrete way.[16]

This attitude, which is nowadays widely, but by no means universally,[17] held, is often expressed, not only by saying that species are more "real" than, e.g., genera, but by saying that specific differences reflect "natural" discontinuities between types of organisms. The latter statement is more accurately put as follows: all taxonomic differences reflect discontinuities in nature (since the cleavage between, say, the Reptilia and the Aves is just as natural as that between *D. simulans* and *D. melanogaster*), but every natural cleavage represents a specific difference. These formulations are admittedly suggestive, but inexact due to the vagueness of the term "natural." If the whole statement is translated into one about "natural kinds" in Mill's sense, it is perhaps clearer. But the fact remains that there are natural kinds of organisms that are not taxa of species rank.

[15] Mayr *et al.*, *Methods and Principles*, pp. 24–25.
[16] Huxley, "Introductory," in *New Systematics*, ed. Huxley, pp. 3–4.
[17] Burma, "Species Concept," *Evolution*, III, 369–70.

The New Systematist verbalizes his attitude toward the species as a special case in defense against a widespread tendency to deny "reality" to all taxa, on the ground that a subjective element enters into their circumscription. It is admitted that the higher taxa are "unreal," but this is denied for species. The difficulty here is, of course, that the term "real" is suggestive of the intent, but hardly adequate for communicating precisely what systematists have in mind. If the denial of reality to all taxa were made on general nominalistic grounds, the denial would carry no weight in scientific circles. This point is underlined by John Gregg's brief but telling argument that, if "species do not exist" means "there is no A such that A is a species," then the statement is clearly false, since, for example, Homo sapiens is a species.[18] But the assertion is made on the grounds of the arbitrary element in all circumscriptions of taxa. Gregg suggests that when a taxonomist asserts (or denies) that a taxon A is "real" he must mean that there is (or is not) a taxonomically adequate category-definition D, and that A satisfies D.[19] If there were such a category-definition, and the taxa of that category satisfied it, those taxa could not be said to be arbitrary. As Gregg points out, his analysis interprets the view that all the higher taxa are unreal, and in addition shows that the taxa of species rank have some claim to reality, since there are definitions of the species category that have at least some limited application.[20]

It seems to me, however, that this analysis does not do full justice to the grounds of the New Systematist's position. There is no fully adequate definition of "species"; and even if a fully adequate definition of, say, "family" were available, I am certain that Huxley and the other exponents of his view would stick by their guns. To insist that the species is more real than the family or the other higher categories (and indeed the subspecific categories) is to hold simply that, at any given time, any member of a species is, *qua* member, a potential mate of a large subclass of that species. Thus the whole species is, so to speak, bound together in a network, the strands of the net representing potential crosses. These strands are largely confined within the limits of the species. The essential point here is that the relation between mates is a biological, dynamic, causal, or if

[18] Gregg, "Taxonomy," *American Naturalist*, LXXXIV, 421–23.
[19] *Ibid.*, p. 433.   [20] *Ibid.*

one prefers, real and objective relation. This is not to say that there are no biological relations between all the members of higher and lower categories; for example, all the members of a genus may be potential or actual competitors for a limited food supply. But, in general, such group-unifying relations are not universally distributed throughout the taxa of a higher rank, and even if they were, it is not essential to the concept of the category of that rank that they be so distributed. In short, all the biological relations which connect together the members of taxa of higher rank do so by historical accident, whereas this is not true of the species. The relations between the members of the higher taxa are not biological, not dynamic, not causal, and in this sense not real and objective; they are historical relations (in so far as the taxa are based upon phylogeny) and relations of abstract morphological similarity. This seems to me the whole content of the New Systematists' position on this point. In practice it is equivalent to Gregg's analysis, since, as I have argued, the relation of potential mating, while not affording a definition of the species category, does afford a criterion of adequacy for any effective definition.

While holding that species are real or objective, the New Systematics admits an element of "subjectivity" in the circumscription of particular species. Tate Regan defined a species as "a community or number of related communities, whose distinctive morphological characters are in the opinion of a competent systematist sufficiently definite to entitle it, or them, to a separate name." [21] J. S. L. Gilmour gives an exactly analogous circular definition; [22] Simpson also emphasizes the subjective element in classifications.[23] But everyone agrees that the empirical material places large constraints upon the systematist's inclinations; in practice, there is remarkable agreement among competent workers, at least in the fairly well worked animal groups. One first examines the material and then, in Huxley's phrase, one exercises "flair." [24]

[21] Quoted in Arkell and Moy-Thomas, "Palaeontology," in *New Systematics,* ed. Huxley, p. 395.

[22] Gilmour, "Taxonomy and Philosophy," in *New Systematics,* ed. Huxley, pp. 468–69.

[23] Simpson, "Principles of Classification," *Bulletin of the American Museum of Natural History,* LXXXV, 5.

[24] Huxley, "Introductory," in *New Systematics,* ed. Huxley, p. 11.

The area in which arbitrary choice is applied is identified in the foregoing analysis. The effective definition of "species," derived from the criteria of adequacy with the help of evolution theory, renders the taxa of species rank polytypic with respect to the class of taxonomic characters. The vague term 'large' enters twice into the definition of a polytypic concept. The species-definition tells a good deal about the makeup of a species, but the systematist must decide just how large "large" is in a particular case, and he must make the circumscription resulting from this decision conform to the criteria of adequacy.

THE POPULATION AS BASIC TAXONOMIC UNIT. There are two further aspects of the New Systematics that may be interpreted in terms of this analysis. The first is that "the population, represented by an adequate sample, the 'series' of the museum worker, has become the basic taxonomic unit." In the old systematics, the specimen was the basic unit.[25] It is difficult to see exactly what is intended here. In so far as populations are classified, the members of the populations are classified as well. In what sense, then, is the population "more basic"? It seems to me that this concept may be interpreted as follows: a reliable species-description cannot be gained through an examination of single or a few specimens; and a species-description is reliable in so far as specimens on which it is based represent an adequate sample of the species; and this requires an adequate sample of the populations of the species. And to be adequate, a sample needs to be large. This follows from the polytypic character of species. In order to utilize a character in a species-description, it must be known that the character is widely distributed in the species, though it need not be universal. The individual specimen, when it is described by a specific concept, is explicitly related to a population or a number of them. Put in other words: though the species-description refers to properties possessed only by specimens, if the description is effective, there must exist populations in which the properties are distributed in the ways entailed by the notion of a polytypic concept.

Both Simpson and Mayr are unequivocal in their denunciation of the "type" or "archetypal" conception of the species, which, they

---

[25] Mayr *et al., Methods and Principles,* p. 13.

maintain, is involved in the view that the individual is the basic taxonomic unit.[26] According to this view, the species is a Platonic Idea, and the morphological species-description the more or less adequate definition of the Idea. The individual is then conceived as approximating more or less closely to the Idea, in so far as it conforms to the morphological description. Individuals are, so to speak, variations on a theme. The difficulties of this from the systematist's point of view are legion. It is a complete mistake to think that morphology is of the essence of a species; species should be regarded as groups of populations, not as abstract ideas; it leads to the temptation to regard forms that are closest to the "ideal" as somehow more fundamental in nature; that different kinds of characters distinguish the taxa of different rank; that the lower taxa have more characters in common than the higher taxa; and finally, it reinforces the view, very widespread, that morphological properties are logically defining characteristics. Simpson specifically attributes this last view to Mayr as a kind of "subconscious hangover" from the old systematics.[27]

It is true that the so-called "type method" is utilized in practical systematics. The "type" of a species is a single individual, the "type" of a genus is a species. But as many writers have pointed out,[28] the type-specimen or taxon is no longer regarded as "typical" of the taxon, or even as the foundation of a taxon E-definition. The type serves the purely practical function of fixing systematic names in case question should arise, e.g., as to whether a newly found population is to be referred to an inadequately described species, or given a new name. Elaborate but necessary conventions have established the rules for solving such problems of nomenclature. Simpson has suggested that the type should frankly be called a "name-bearer," or "onomotophore."

THE USE OF QUANTITATIVE TECHNIQUES. The second aspect of the

[26] *Ibid.*, p. 15; Simpson, "Principles of Classification," *Bulletin of the American Museum of Natural History*, LXXXV, 3–4; and Simpson, *Major Features*, pp. 340–41.

[27] Simpson, *Major Features*, p. 341, n. 2.

[28] Mayr, *Systematics*, p. 15; and Mayr *et al.*, *Methods and Principles*, pp. 236–45.

New Systematics I wish to examine in this connection is its widespread adoption of quantitative and especially statistical techniques.

Body measures such as gross weights, absolute lengths, and ratios, scale or bristle counts, etc., are of course legitimate taxonomic characters in any interpretation of taxonomy. But it is a well-known fact that, for various reasons, any measure of an organism subject to continuous variation will show a range of variation in a population. If, say, a taxonomist wishes to use an *interval* as a character in a species-description, he is faced with a severe logical problem if such characters are regarded as defining the species. For the interval may overlap the corresponding interval in other species, and many individuals in the species may fall outside the interval.

From the point of view we have developed, this difficulty may be overcome. Possession of a magnitude within the interval may simply be regarded as one of the properties in the G-class of the polytypic species-definition. This kind of procedure is in fact employed for the solution of a number of types of difficult taxonomic problems. Suppose that two sympatric forms are believed to be specifically distinct, that a reliable morphological description of them is desired, but the search for diagnostic characters-in-common fails. The systematist may take a large sample of the forms, and without segregating them, make a number of measures. If the sample contains two species, a plot of the frequency of a value of the measure versus the value will give a curve with two distinct humps—on the assumption that the mean of the measure differs in the two species. If the curve is approximately normal, we are dealing with only one form. O. W. Richards cites a study of this type performed on the members of herring shoals. The systematist was able to assign a given fish to the proper shoal on the basis of twenty-four to sixty-five measures: the measures of the specimen are taken, and the specimen is assigned to shoal (population) A if the sum of the squares of the deviations of the measures from the means of A gives a minimum. Less reliability is of course attained with fewer measures.[29] If we grant (which cannot be granted without further evidence) that the two shoals are specifically distinct, the class of measures may be

[29] Richards, "Formation of Species," in *Evolution*, ed. De Beer, p. 104.

justly interpreted as the G-class of a polytypic E-definition. Each measure would be stated as an interval, probably in terms of the mean and the standard deviation.

HIGHER TAXONOMIC CATEGORIES
AND TAXA OF HIGHER RANK

It will be maintained that neither the categories nor taxa of higher rank are W-defined; that the categories are not even E-defined; but that the taxa are E-defined and polytypic. There are, however, criteria of adequacy for the E-definition of the higher taxa analogous to those for the E-definition of taxa of specific rank. I will argue that these theses successfully interpret both the practice and the methodological views of the New Systematics, and that they make clear two important features of the taxonomic system. These are the fundamental role played by the species in the system, and the essentially systematic import (in the wider sense of the term "systematic") of the higher categories and taxa, i.e., a given taxon occupies its place in the hierarchy and is effectively defined in the manner adopted, not only because the group of animals possesses such-and-such properties, but because other taxa are assigned the places they occupy. The whole system is, as it were, built up by a series of successive approximations.

It is universally accepted that the higher categories are not precisely definable at all.[30] Tentative definitions of "genus" are sometimes offered. It has been suggested that the genus is definable in terms of the morphology of the "type-species." [31] This definition has been abandoned along with the type-conception of the taxon. Other "definitions," e.g., Mayr's and Gilmour's, are recognized by their authors to be vague and essentially circular. Categories higher than genus are usually left untouched.

It is true, however, that the systematist is not left entirely to his own devices in defining the higher taxa and assigning them their place in the hierarchy. These constraining factors may be stated in

---

[30] For explicit statements, see Mayr *et al., Methods and Principles,* p. 48; Gilmour, "Taxonomy and Philosophy," in *New Systematics,* ed. Huxley, p. 469; Mayr, *Systematics,* p. 283; and Gregg, "Taxonomy," *American Naturalist,* LXXXIV, 433.

[31] This possibility is discussed by Mayr, *Systematics,* p. 283.

terms of criteria of adequacy for taxon E-definition. They may be
stated in such a way that they hold for taxa of all ranks up to and
including the phyla.

1) Every taxon must be monophyletic
2) Every taxon must be polytypic with respect to a set of morphological characters
3) No polytypic group is to be assigned status as a taxon of rank
   j if it can reasonably be assigned to rank j — 1

The following points should be noticed about this list. There is
no reference to a "biological" criterion, as is the case with the criteria
for species–E-definitions; this in part explains the view that the
higher categories do not exist "in nature." The first two appear to
be perfectly precise, but as I shall show, the first is imprecise because of an essential vagueness in the term "monophyletic." The
third is very vague, but it is a genuine criterion that is easier to apply in practice than might appear. It is of course assumed that no
classification will violate the logical properties of the taxonomic
system outlined above. The three criteria will be discussed in turn.

THE MONOPHYLY OF TAXA. This criterion embodies the view, almost universally held, that the taxonomic system should be "based
on phylogeny." [32] That all taxa should be monophyletic perhaps
goes much further than this, but it is the expressed ideal of
taxonomic workers, although practice may fall short of the ideal.
In spite of the importance of the notion of monophyly in the discussion of the "natural" or phylogenetic system, I have not seen an
accurate analysis of it. Gilmour points out that the notion is widely
misunderstood, and the misunderstanding has done considerable
damage.[33] Since a precise meaning is necessary for an understanding of the first criterion, I shall present an analysis based upon suggestions of Simpson.[34] A taxon of any rank will be said to be

---

[32] Haeckel was the classical exponent of this view. For modern statements,
see Mayr, *Systematics*, p. 277; Simpson, "Principles of Classification," *Bulletin
of the American Museum of Natural History*, LXXXV, 4; Simpson, *Major
Features*, p. 348; Mayr *et al.*, *Methods and Principles*, pp. 41–46, 53;
Sprague, "Taxonomic Botany," in *New Systematics*, ed. Huxley, p. 434; and
Calman, "View of Taxonomy," in *New Systematics*, ed. Huxley, pp. 455–59.
[33] Gilmour, "Taxonomy and Philosophy," in *New Systematics*, ed. Huxley,
pp. 469–71.
[34] Simpson, *Major Features*, pp. 348–49.

monophyletic at the level of taxa of rank j whenever each member of the taxon is either a first-generation descendant of members of that taxon, or a first-generation descendant of members of a distinct taxon of rank j.[35] On this definition, every taxon is monophyletic at some taxonomic level; on the other hand, if individual lineages are not grouped on some basis, every taxon is hopelessly polyphyletic. For the purposes of the criterion, a taxon is regarded as monophyletic without a qualification if it is monophyletic at the species level.

It must be admitted that the taxonomic system as a whole does not conform to this criterion. Simpson points out, for instance, that in all probability the Mammalia, a taxon of class level, so far from being monophyletic at the species level, is at best monophyletic at the class level, since a number of reptilian orders probably crossed over into the mammal group.[36] In the words of F. A. Bather, "The whole of our System, from the great Phyla to the very unit cells, is riddled through and through with polyphyly and convergence." [37] According to Simpson, the ideal of monophyly is approached well enough for most practical purposes if every taxon of rank j is monophyletic at the level of taxa of rank j — 1.[38]

The notion of monopoly is no more precise than the notion of a species. This means that in so far as there is doubt that a given ancestral group is a species, there will be doubt as to whether the descendants constitute a monophyletic group. It should be emphasized that monophyly at any taxonomic level is insufficient grounds on which to base a classification. Even perfect knowledge of descent leaves room for individual taste; [39] the point is elegantly demonstrated in a diagram by Mayr.[40]

THE POLYTYPY OF TAXA. Two comments need to be made about the

---

[35] This definition avoids the ambiguity of statements such as: "Only one lineage leads into a monophyletic group," or, "Each individual must be traceable to a single population (or pair)."

[36] Simpson, *Major Features*, pp. 348–49.

[37] Bather, "Biological Classification," *Quarterly Journal of the Geological Society*, LXXXIII, ci. Quoted by Gilmour, "Taxonomy and Philosophy," in *New Systematics*, ed. Huxley, p. 471.

[38] Simpson, *Major Features*, p. 349.

[39] Simpson, "Principles of Classification," *Bulletin of the American Museum of Natural History*, LXXXV, 5.

[40] Mayr, *Systematics*, p. 282.

second criterion. First, morphological characters were singled out for inclusion in a criterion of adequacy because morphological characters are in fact the basis of diagnostic procedures in the higher taxa, whereas this is not the case with species. Moreover, this does not imply that only morphological characters are to be considered in constructing higher taxa-descriptions. Relevant geographical data deserve, in the opinion of Simpson, at least equal weight. He notes that on the basis of sheer morphology, unclouded by considerations of phylogeny and geography, a thylacine (a marsupial carnivore) shows more affinities with the wolf than with the kangaroo.[41] The important point is that the weight assigned morphological characters is evaluated in the light of phylogeny, geography, physiology—in short, all those characters which can themselves be assigned weight on the basis of phylogeny.

Second, the question might arise whether the requirement that the higher taxa be polytypic is not unnecessarily weak. Would it be unreasonable to require that the higher taxa should be E-defined by a Boolean product of morphological characters? The same arguments on this point that apply to species apply as well to the higher taxa. Moreover, it can be shown that some of the higher taxa are fully polytypic with respect to the morphological characters actually employed in their E-definitions, i.e., that no diagnostic characters are in fact found in all the taxa. Simpson demonstrates that of all the diagnostic characters proposed (in an independent investigation) for the ungulates some are either possessed by certain carnivores, or are lacked by groups of ungulates; and common diagnostic characters cannot be found in the Equidae or in the fissiped carnivores.[42]

THE RANKING OF TAXA. The third criterion is accepted in theory, but often violated in practice. The criterion is partially justified on the ground that a category of rank j should have fewer taxa than a category of rank j — 1 if the system is really to effect a simplification in terminology. The vagueness of this criterion is unavoidable because there are no general rules that specify when it is "reason-

[41] Simpson, "Principles of Classification," *Bulletin of the American Museum of Natural History*, LXXXV, 8.

[42] Simpson, *Major Features*, pp. 343–44.

able" to assign a group to a lower rank. It is possible, however, to specify in a general way what factors the taxonomist takes into account. Suppose the question is whether or not to assign a group to the ordinal or family level. Granted that the group satisfies the first two criteria, the taxonomist first inspects the predescribed orders of the relevant class or subclass. The group need not be included in an order as a family simply because it answers to the morphological description of that order, since the description can easily be modified—but the description can be so modified only if the monophyletic nature of the order is not unduly jeopardized. This of course is a matter of delicate judgment. The lagomorphs were assigned to an order for this reason: the rodentia, with the lagomorphs included, turned out to be polyphyletic at the ordinal level. More importantly, however, the taxonomist considers the taxa within the group in question. In the extreme case, the group in question may show such divergence that the only reasonable procedure, in view of the existing classifications of neighboring orders, is to distinguish a number of taxa of family rank within the group; this constitutes grounds (not decisive to be sure) for making the group an order, or a suborder. At the other extreme, if the group can be well classified with the help only of taxa of species and generic rank, it is reasonable to make it a family, and it would be made a family if its including order were not rendered polyphyletic. This kind of taxonomic reshuffle is constantly occurring, on the basis of new discoveries and in accordance with the "lumper" or "splitter" tastes of the student.

There are two interesting consequences of the fact that a consideration of the classification within a group and of neighboring groups is necessary before a rank may be assigned to the group. The first is that there is no such thing as an "ordinal," "class," etc., character, since whether or not a given character is diagnostic for an order or a class does not depend upon the character as such, but ultimately upon a whole taxonomic system. Second, a group that is E-defined by reference to a fixed G-class of morphological properties may change from a lower to a higher rank with time. This can happen if a particular species is the beginner of a long and successful series of adaptive radiations. When the species first appeared, it

was not, say, a genus simply because it was E-defined by this
G-class, but its descendants, all of whom answer to the E-definition,
might well be a genus.

The value of a character is determined primarily by the size of the group
which exhibits it. The same is true for categorical rank. If the pterosaurs
were still alive today and were as numerous and as rich in species as the
birds, they would very likely be considered a separate class and not one
of the reptilian orders. If, on the other hand, birds had become extinct
at the *Archaeopteryx* stage, it is very probable that *Archaeopteryx* would
be listed merely as an aberrant order of feathered reptiles.[43]

We have still to consider the sense in which species are the fundamental taxa in the systematic hierarchy. The following points are
relevant in this connection. The species is the only category which
is E-defined, and its E-definition is made possible only by availability of the "biological species-criterion." And species are the only
taxa whose E-definitions are not governed by a criterion of adequacy that can be applied only after inspection of large segments of
the systematic hierarchy. The species provides an anchor on which
the whole system rests, because we do not have to ask ourselves
(except in exceptional cases) whether a group should be referred
to specific or generic rank. Without the biological criterion, there
would be no way of deciding whether or not a chain of local populations constitute a genus or a species, and this uncertainty could
infect the classification of the higher taxa on the levels immediately above it. Finally, the concept of the species provides the
most convenient tool for the definition of "monophyly."

I shall now summarize the conclusions and state briefly what I
take to be the wider significance of these analyses.

1. The concept of the species category is, in the sense defined
in Chapter II, both historical and functional. It is historical because
it is logically impossible for a taxon to be a species unless it is monophyletic with respect to a single interbreeding population; functional, because it is logically impossible for a taxon to be a species
unless its members contribute to the function of self-reproduction of
its component populations. These conditions do not constitute a

[43] Mayr, *Systematics*, p. 298.

W-definition of "species," but they do serve as conditions of adequacy for a polytypic E-definition. The taxonomic system well illustrates one possible scientific role of historical and functional concepts: though these concepts are formed in reference to empirical materials that do not themselves play a causal role in phenomena described with the help of these concepts, W-definitions or W-defining criteria of adequacy do provide rules for the derivation of concepts that will help in these respects. "Species" is one such concept.

2. The taxa of specific rank are also historical and functional, since the W-defining criteria of adequacy for the species-definition serve as well as criteria for E-definition of the particular species. The higher categories are historical but not functional, and they are neither W- nor E-defined. The higher taxa are likewise historical but not functional, and they are E-defined by reference to a class of taxonomic properties. Thus, to apply any taxon to a specimen, e.g., to say "x is a member of *D. simulans* and of the Arthropoda," is to make implicit reference to two distinct sets of empirical materials that need bear no causal relations to the specimen at hand. In the case of the taxa of species rank, those materials include both the P-events that insure that the species is monophyletic, and the population(s) with which the specimen is a potential interbreeder. In the case of a higher taxon, the materials are, again, the P-events and (here is the sense in which the higher taxa differ "in kind" from species) the neighboring taxa in the systematic hierarchy, together with the lower taxa included within the taxon. The significance of the historical and functional aspects of taxa is the same as that described for the species category.

3. The species category and all taxa of all ranks are polytypic, the former with respect to the taxonomist's "species-criteria," the latter with respect to the set of taxonomic characters. Some of the higher taxa are known to be, in all probability, fully polytypic. It follows that there is still a third set of empirical materials implicitly involved in the application of a taxon to a specimen. This is the distribution of the taxonomic characters throughout the taxon. It follows in addition that to apply a taxon to a specimen is not to attribute any particular taxonomic character to it, in the way in

which, e.g., applying the term 'lever' to a physical system attributes to that system the power of multiplying mechanical advantage. This places certain constraints on the use of polytypic concepts in the formation of laws.

Nevertheless, the taxa are exceedingly useful, and in a sense their polytypic nature is unavoidable in the light of the empirical facts, once the scientist has committed himself to the construction of a system which combines convenience of diagnosis with the lumping together of organisms with the greatest number of shared properties. Ultimately, the grounds of their polytypic nature may be put in the following way. The taxonomic characters are known to be dependent on the set of genes possessed by the organism. Consider any taxon T; let G be the class of properties defined as "possessing gene A_1," "possessing gene A_2," [44] etc.; and let the class of A's be the class of all genes possessed by the members of T. Then it is very possible that T will be fully polytypic with respect to G; and in the higher categories T will be fully polytypic with respect to a relatively quite small subclass of G.

4. It seems to me that the systematic categories and the taxa qualify preeminently as "specifically biological" concepts. Their extensions are biological systems; they are defined in the modes I distinguished as more characteristic of biology than of the other natural sciences; they are concepts whose "significance" cannot be understood apart from the wider context in which they figure; and finally, there seems to be no clear sense in which it would be possible to state necessary and sufficient conditions for applying them in physicochemical terms, if by that is meant the terms ordinarily employed in the language of physics and chemistry. The point which I wish to emphasize above all is the theoretical role played by the historical and functional W-defining criteria of adequacy. They add to the concepts a surplus of meaning not needed in many of the applications of the concept, but they are principles or rules directing the effective definition of concepts applicable under the widest range of circumstances. Having adopted such criteria, whether or not E-definitions will be polytypic with respect to the properties on which the E-definitions are based is then an em-

[44] The A's are names of alleles, not individual names.

pirical question. There is nothing in the notion of a functional or historical concept that requires that they be polytypic. But it is well to recognize that the taxa are polytypic with respect to the taxonomic characters, and that this situation is not only legitimate, but desirable.

CHAPTER V

Genetic Analysis
and Explanation

The discussion of the logic of historical explanation in the biological sciences has been hampered by two confusions. The first is the failure to distinguish between two logically distinct patterns of historical explanation; the second is the consequent failure to see that the two main types of "histories" which are of interest to biologists, ontogenies and phylogenies, present phenomena which are subject to historical explanation in different patterns. The task of this chapter is to distinguish the two patterns, and to apply the distinction to the problem of ontogenetic and phylogenetic explanations in biology and to the question of the roles of historical concepts and of models in historical explanations.

I shall use the term 'genetic' rather than 'historical' in referring to explanations or descriptions of phenomena other than those of human history. To one of the patterns of historical explanation, accordingly, I shall henceforth deny both the title of 'historical' and that of 'explanation,' using instead the term 'genetic analysis.' Throughout this study the term 'explanation' is reserved, arbitrarily perhaps, for sets of propositions that meet the formal requirements of the Humean Pattern. There is a widespread and perfectly legitimate type of historical investigation yielding sets of propositions that may impart understanding, but which do not conform to the Humean Pattern. On the other hand, there is a type of historical investigation that does yield Humean explanations; I shall call these 'genetic explanations.' I trust that the context will in each case show when I am using the term 'genetic' in the sense broader than its customary signification in biology.

In biological theory, as against the other disciplines concerned with histories, the problem of origins is complicated by the fact that there are two distinct types of development shown by organic systems, embryonic development and the evolution of populations. It is evident that there are important logical relations between the concepts of ontogeny and phylogeny, and biologists have made it evident that there are also important empirical relations between types of ontogenies and phylogenies. There has been considerable confusion as to what these relations are and how they are to be interpreted. One need only point to the view, held by most post-Darwinian embryologists up to the time of His and Roux, that all explanation in embryology is "phylogenetic," and to L. S. Berg's doctrine that both ontogeny and phylogeny are regulated by exactly the same laws.[1] Part of the task of this chapter will be to formulate a sufficient number of the logical and empirical relations between ontogeny and phylogeny to assess the significance of the various claims that phylogeny throws light on ontogeny, and vice versa. This is of course a question in the logic of historical explanation. It will be shown that "phylogenetic explanation" is either pseudo-explanation, or genetic explanation in the Humean Pattern—in fact, a subclass of model explanations. The notion of a model will be used in analyzing Haeckel's Biogenetic Law and in general the phenomena of recapitulation.

GENETIC ANALYSIS

"Genetic analysis" may be defined as follows. If we let E be the *analysandum*, a genetic analysis consists in exhibiting E as the outcome of a set of chains of events. Each chain, for the purposes of the analysis, is regarded as initiating with a single event, here called a beginner-event; each link in each chain is causally connected with the previous link, and is either contiguous with it or temporally overlaps it. A single event is the last link of all the chains (i.e., the links converge on one event); E is this last event, a spatiotemporal part of it, or a property of it or its spatiotemporal parts.

This definition will require some elucidation. The 'link' and 'chain' terminology is simply a device for shortening exposition.

---

[1] Berg, *Nomogenesis*, trans. Rostovtsow, pp. 156–57. Quoted in Fothergill, *Historical Aspects*, p. 170.

Any statement in which these expressions occur could be translated, in obvious ways, into statements about events and their spatial and temporal relations. The important point is that the analysis calls attention to a continuous development or persistence in the objects and events that are genetically related to E. The type of events which are selected, e.g., ontogenies; cell divisions; geological occurrences such as ice ages, inundations, formation of landbridges; chemical events such as changes in concentrations, formation of precipitates; and so on, is determined by the analytic problem at hand. It is required, in order for the analysis to be adequate, that the events be arranged in sequences as described, and that E *can* be exhibited as the outcome of the sequences. Consider the example used by Woodger to illustrate this type of genetic analysis.

For example the tortuous course taken by a nerve or an artery may strike us as strange and we seek an explanation (i.e., for why it does not conform to our expectations) and we find one if it can be shown that in the course of individual development this state of affairs has been brought about by the shifting of neighbouring parts.[2]

E is a constellation of anatomical details about an organism at a stage of its development. The beginner-event (there is only one chain in this simple case) may be regarded as a very short temporal stretch in the past history of the organism. The subsequent links are subsequent time stretches in the developmental history. The chain of events in the example are on a high "level of organization." It is certainly true that the morphology of an organism at a developmental stage is the outcome of a series of cell divisions, i.e., of a chain of events that the embryologist would call histological elaboration and differentiation. But the technical task of exhibiting E as the outcome of a series of cell divisions would be beyond the bounds of all human patience, and moreover, a thankless task. Similar remarks apply to events on the biochemical level. It might be the case that a causal explanation of E could be obtained by attention to the events at the cellular or biochemical level, but the embryologist is not attempting a causal explanation. In trying to explain the morphology of an organ such as an artery, the appropriate level of analysis is defined by events we should call "organ-formation."

[2] Woodger, *Biological Principles*, p. 394.

The meaning of "appropriate" in this context is given by the practical requirement of actually exhibiting the continuity between E and the beginner-events. The beginner-event is not itself the *analysans:* this consists in the description of the chain of events leading from the beginner to E inclusive. Of course, in practice the investigator need not enumerate all the links in the chain, but only a sufficient number to make clear the direction of change whose outcome is E. How many are necessary will again depend on the problem under consideration.

It is necessary to see exactly how genetic analyses of this type differ from "causal" explanations. According to a widely held view, with which I agree, causal explanations are explanations in the Humean Pattern. The peculiarities of genetic analysis may accordingly be examined by comparison with the Humean Pattern. The chief difference, which is all-important, may be put as follows: in the Humean Pattern it is not only presupposed that the *explanans* is causally connected with the state of affairs described in terms of the initial and boundary conditions, but the connection is explicitly stated in the form of a set of laws. The initial and boundary conditions are shown, with the help of the laws, to be sufficient for the occurrence of the *explanandum.* In genetic analysis, on the other hand, it is neither presupposed nor (although it might be true) stated that any link in a chain from beginner-event to E is sufficient for the occurrence of the next link. On the contrary, it is usually assumed and in most cases known, on rough inductive grounds, that any link in the chain is jointly caused by a set of factors, only some of which are included in the previous link. To give a genetic analysis much less information suffices than would be required to show that each link is sufficient for the occurrence of the next, since this would require knowledge of universal laws. It is a commonplace—that nevertheless ought to be taken very seriously in this context—that the formulation of general statements that will meet the stringent condition of unrestricted universality required of a law can in general be achieved only with the aid of sets of concepts especially constructed for the purpose. The concepts employed in much historical analysis have not been constructed for this purpose, but are imported from the

common language, from other disciplines, or, in the case of many
of the concepts of embryology, are constructed for the purposes
of historical analysis itself. To be sure, general propositions can be
formulated with their help, but ordinarily these are not laws, but
only rough statements of tendency or relatively regular conjunction. To put the point another way, we often know that A is causally
connected with B, e.g., that a blow of the sledge hammer is causally
connected with the shattering of an egg, without being aware of
the laws that would enable Humean explanation of B by reference
to factors present in A and B. Suppose that one of the morphological
details to be explained (in Woodger's example) is the fact that the
artery by-passes an organ on a particular side rather than, e.g., pass-
ing through it, or encircling it on a different side. Let the beginner-
event be a prior stretch of the organism's history in which the organ has just begun to appear, and lies alongside the artery. As the
organ grows, it makes contact with the artery, and gradually dis-
places a segment into the form of a semicircle. Can we say that the
growth of the organ is sufficient to displace the artery in exactly
this fashion? We certainly have no laws that tell us it is sufficient;
a priori we could just as well expect the organ to envelop the artery,
or to form a groove for it; indeed, cases of this kind are known to
the embryologist. Nevertheless, as a matter of historical fact, this
does not happen, and no one would seriously dispute that the growing organ is part of the cause of the displacement of the artery.

One requirement for genetic analysis is that the links in the
chain of events are in fact causally related, not that the causal relationship be specifiable in a theory. This is completely consistent
with Hempel's view that "in no other way than by reference to empirical laws can the assertion of a causal connection between certain events be scientifically substantiated."[3] The point of the
genetic analysis is not to ascertain that events are causally connected, but rather to exhibit the character of events as the outcome
of a continuous transformation analyzable into a chain of events
that *are* causally connected. Of course, it is a psychological fact that
no one would feel well satisfied with a proffered historical analysis

[3] Hempel, "General Laws in History," in *Philosophical Analysis,* ed. Feigl
and Sellars, p. 461, n. 1.

unless he believed, however vaguely and implicitly, that the linked events are causally connected; but, then, spatiotemporal continuity of an intimate kind is usually taken as evidence of a causal connection, in the absence of positive reason to think otherwise. It is also true that an investigator could not find his way about in a complex historical situation without a great deal of prior knowledge of causal connections.

Philosophers of empirical persuasion commonly emphasize the role of general laws in genetic explanation. Hempel regards genetic explanation as an outline of a Humean explanation, a sketch which needs filling out through further research, and which itself directs the lines such research should take.[4] Nagel holds there is no warrant for regarding the pattern of historical explanations as fundamentally different from the pattern of explanation in the natural sciences, on the grounds that both utilize singular and general statements that may indeed, in both cases, be partially implicit or tacit.[5] There is no doubt that this point of view needs emphasizing if only to counteract the influences of an invidious distinction between so-called "nomothetic" and "ideographic" sciences. But it should be recognized that the notion of "tacit" or "implicit" use of laws in an explanation is by no means clear if the laws are unknown. It is necessary to distinguish the fact that certain general laws, which may be entirely unknown, must be exemplified in a situation under analysis from the fact of the actual employment of general laws in analysis. Moreover, it is important to recognize the sense in which genetic analyses "presuppose" general laws. To say that event A is causally connected with event B is to say that there are a set of principles which would show that A, together perhaps with other factors, is sufficient for B, but if such a set of principles is not known, it is using language oddly to say that anyone who asserts "A causes B" is "implicitly asserting" all the laws that the truth of this statement presupposes. I do not see how this could be distinguished in principle from the view that one who asserts "X is a man" is implicitly asserting everything that is true of a man. Moreover, in genetic analysis, it is not necessarily

[4] *Ibid.*, pp. 465–66.
[5] Nagel, "Logic of Historical Analysis," *Scientific Monthly*, LXXIV, 163.

asserted (though it may be) that the links in the chain are causally connected; it is merely presupposed in the sense that if they are not causally connected, the alleged analysis is faulty. Knowledge of causal connections, in other words, plays a psychological role in the construction and adoption of genetic analysis, but no necessary role in the logical pattern of the analysis.

W. B. Gallie emphasizes that "characteristically historical (or genetic) explanations" establish some kind of continuity or persistence between prior conditions and a subsequent result, and that they are not "sufficiency explanations," although he grants that they do contain a "latent causal reference." [6] According to Gallie, genetic

explanation commences from our recognition of the event to be explained as being of such a kind that *some one* of a disjunction of describable conditions is necessary to its occurrence; and the explanation consists in elucidating *which one* of this disjunctive set is applicable, in the sense of being necessary, to the event in question.[7]

Gallie is here attempting to draw a distinction between the pattern of explanation in the genetic and natural sciences. On the basis of this statement he points out, quite correctly, that such genetic explanations do not have predictive power, and, also correctly, that a genetic explanation cannot be regarded as a "retrodiction." His grounds for the latter statement consist in the observation that the term "retrodiction" is reserved for the case in which the prior occurrence is taken as both necessary and sufficient condition for the subsequent one, whereas genetic explanation lays down only a necessary condition.[8] The conclusion is well taken, but it does not follow from Gallie's own analysis. For if we say that one or another of a disjunction of events is necessary for the occurrence of a subsequent event E, we cannot then say that one of its disjuncts is necessary for E, since E could occur even though a given disjunct fails to occur. Therefore, on Gallie's own account, the *explanans* of a genetic explanation does not lay down a necessary condition of the *explanandum*. Secondly, if A is necessary for B, the occurrence of B is sufficient ground for a retrodiction. The requirement that

[6] Gallie, "Explanations," *Mind*, LXIV, 165, 167.
[7] *Ibid.*, p. 161.   [8] *Ibid.*, p. 167.

A also be sufficient for B is altogether too strong. The Humean Pattern itself, in pure form, does not in general explain B by laying down necessary conditions for B, but only sufficient ones.

Gallie's intent—which, if I read him correctly, corresponds to my own—can more accurately be realized by stating that genetic explanation, or analysis, relates E to a prior beginner-event (or events) through a continuous chain of events (or number of chains), each link of which is sufficient for the occurrence of the succeeding link (but is not necessarily known to be so), or else is sufficient in conjunction with further (unspecified) factors.

A proffered genetic analysis can be challenged on two general grounds. First, it might be claimed that it does not really exhibit E as the outcome of a continuous process. For instance, suppose an ecologist explains the distribution of a species in terms of a place of origin and subsequent migrations of populations. A critic might argue that the place of origin is mistaken or that the stages of migration postulated did not occur in just that way. This kind of challenge can only be met by appeal to further historical data.

Or a critic might object that somewhere in the chain of events connecting the original population with the contemporary ones, a sequence has been postulated that is not causally connected, i.e., that the conditions of distribution at time t_0, together with other factors, are not sufficient for the occurrence of the given distribution at a later time t_1. Suppose that the distribution at t_1 includes large lacunae not present at t_0: the challenger is asserting that conditions at t_0 are insufficient to account for the lacunae. This kind of objection can be met by an appeal to further historical data, together with general statements that tend to show that the conditions were sufficient. One may appeal to evidence showing a predator, or lack of appropriate food, etc., in the lacunae. He need not, however, show that the presence of a predator is in fact sufficient to account for the lacunae; this would require knowledge of ecological laws of a finer grain than those available. He need only enlarge the questioned link, describe more aspects of it, to the point where opposition is either silenced or made academic. He must, however, appeal to general principles, e.g., "predators discourage immigration," and not merely historical data.

GENETIC ANALYSIS, HISTORICAL LAWS,
AND HISTORICAL CONCEPTS

We shall now consider how this analysis of genetic explanation is related to the problem of historical law, and how both are related to the nature and function of historical concepts, as I have defined this term.

As Woodger points out,[9] genetic analyses in embryology of the type quoted are generalizable, i.e., it can be shown that the whole continuous chain of events is a member of a class of similar chains, or put more strongly, of a class of chains identical in those respects mentioned in the genetic explanation. If we learn that each time a beginner-event of type A occurs, chains of events are initiated that yield E as an outcome, we may formulate a general law-like statement. This can be achieved only if the beginners are so selected that they include, or are universally conjoined with, all the factors that are jointly sufficient for the occurrence of the first intermediate links in the chain. It must further be the case that each link is sufficient for the occurrence of the succeeding links, or else that the succeeding links are paralleled by contemporaneous changes that cooperate in forming sufficient conditions for the occurrence of the next link. If the sequence is temporally long, and the systems undergoing change are subject to much outside influence, it can be seen how seldom we could reasonably expect to realize this ideal in practical enquiry. Where the interval is short, or where the systems are relatively well isolated, we can and do achieve the formulation of strict laws.

Suppose now that we discover that a beginner not always, but for the most part, initiates a chain of events that yields an outcome of type E, e.g., that fertilization of an egg of type A begins an ontogeny that yields a metazoan animal of type B. This is a fundamental form of law in embryology, where B is a taxon. Similar laws where A and B are genotypes and phenotypes are shown by Woodger to be fundamental in genetical theory.[10] As it is stated, the "law" is not universal, however, since not all zygotes develop, and some

[9] Woodger, *Biological Principles*, p. 394.
[10] Woodger, *Biology and Language*, p. 128.

develop anomalously. This difficulty can in some cases be overcome simply by the adoption of restrictions on the scope of the law. In embryology, the restrictions that are actually introduced by Woodger are these: it is stated that if the A-type egg develops in environments of type C, then it yields a B-type organism. The explicit restriction that the law holds only for eggs that develop is odd, in that it does not rule out a previously specifiable subclass of A-type eggs; therefore the law does not enable the biologist to predict that he will get a B-type organism in a C-type environment from the relevant type of egg. The restriction is not without physical precedent, however: compare the thermodynamic principle that if there is an exchange of energy between the parts of an isolated system, the amount of free energy in the system will decrease.

If we grant that the embryologist can, by suitable specification of "A-type eggs" and "C-type environment," write universally true statements linking fertilization with type of morphology at later developmental stages, what justification would there be for calling them "historical"? Philosophers have used this term to refer to two distinct types of laws, both of which differ from embryological laws. Some have restricted the term to laws relating to human events and institutions, e.g., "cultures, states, nations, occupations, classes, etc." [11] The natural sciences do not employ historical laws in this sense. The term is also used to refer to laws, mathematical in form, which give the value of a variable as a function of the values that a set of variables assume over a time interval.[12] The function may require integration of the variables over the interval, or substitution of sets of discrete values for a succession of times or intervals. Examples of the latter can be found in behavior theory, e.g., the formula, which B. F. Skinner expresses only graphically, that connects the rate of change of frequency of bar-pressing in a Skinner box at t_k with the frequency of responses negatively correlated with reinforcement in a set of subintervals from t_0 to t_k.[13] The embryological law is not of this type.

[11] Zilsel, "Historico-sociological Laws," in *Philosophy of Science*, ed. Feigl and Brodbeck, p. 716.
[12] Bergmann, "Problems of Psychology," in *Philosophy of Science*, ed. Feigl and Brodbeck, p. 634.
[13] Skinner, *Behavior of Organisms*, pp. 161–62.

If we make connection of an earlier with a later state the criterion of a historical law, we would, to be sure, discriminate two classes of laws, and the laws of the types described, together with the embryological laws, would be included among the historical laws. But many laws not usually regarded as historical would also be included, namely, all the so-called "laws of succession" as against the laws of coincidence of characters. For these reasons it would seem best to deny the term "historical" to the embryological laws.

Nevertheless, embryological laws, and a number of other types of laws such as the rules of trend that were at one time so dear to paleontologists (e.g., Williston's law), possess some features that ought to be noticed, even though they are not sufficiently important to warrant use of a special term. Such laws are applicable to relatively long-term sequences. In this respect they are like many ordinary laws of succession. But they are not applicable to very short-term sequences, and here they differ from the typical laws of succession utilized in physical theory. They are commonly discovered through generalization of genetic analyses. This is true of Williston's and many embryological laws. There is, however, no general rule about the way they must be discovered. The law which states that populations geographically isolated will develop genetic isolating mechanisms was inferred from the principles of experimental genetics together with certain facts of natural history. The existence of clines such as those described in the ecological rules of Bergmann, Allen, and Gloger may be explained by postulating long-term laws connecting the state of locally restricted populations to their state after their growth and spread. In these cases a "historical" hypothesis is inferred from the facts about population distribution, rather than from historical data. Finally, long-term laws describe macroscopic phenomena that are dependent upon the operation of mechanisms which are microscopic with respect to the level of analysis appropriate to the macroscopic law. Moreover, they are commonly recognized to be macroscopic, and in general it is possible to formulate a sketch of the way in which the law depends upon the microscopic mechanisms. These facts confer a peculiar status on these laws: until the details of the microscopic mechanisms are known, i.e., until a reduction of the law has been achieved, some scope restrictions may

be purely *ad hoc;* and one cannot be sure that some restrictions are
not too stringent and that some other restrictions have not been
overlooked. A scope restriction is *ad hoc* unless there exists a theory
that permits derivation of the law together with the scope restrictions. To illustrate this point suppose that all populations of type A,
if they survive, develop into a set of populations of type B, that A
and B are defined by reference to macroscopic properties of populations, such as the presence of morphological clines within them.
Suppose—what would probably be the case—that this law is exemplified only in populations with a particular genetic system, interacting with particular environmental conditions; and that it is in principle possible to explain the law by reference to a set of factors that
refer to the genetic system and the environment, together with the
relevant laws. We could then schematize the law, together with a
set of restrictive conditions derived from the theory explaining the
law, as, "Under circumstances q_1, q_2, . . . , q_n, if A, then B," where
the q's refer, not to macroscopic properties of populations exclusively, but in part to the properties of the genetic system. So long
as the relevant q's are unknown, the law may be stated in the form,
"Under circumstances C_1, C_2, . . . , C_n, if A, then B," where the C's
are chosen to rule out counterinstances observed on the macroscopic
level, i.e., they may specify *taxa* (this is the commonest case), a
method of seed dispersal or pollination, a way of life such as para-
sitism, etc. In so far as these restrictions are adequate it will be due
to the presumably contingent fact that the populations so restricted
possess the requisite genetic system, and are found in the requisite
environments. In other words, such scope restrictions are not part
of the theory that is believed to be capable of explaining the laws.
This point is important for the following reason: biologists often
speak as if it is possible, for all macroscopic phenomena, to construct
theories on the macroscopic level with comparable degrees of theoretical articulation attainable in the physical sciences. An essential
aspect of such highly articulated theories lies in their provision for
introducing restrictions on the generality of their laws. There is, it
seems to me, good grounds for skepticism concerning the possibility
of achieving very general theories when the operation of microscopic mechanisms known to be relevant are poorly understood.

More strongly stated, it is possible that there are no laws statable at the macroscopic level which are capable of describing some aspects of macroscopic phenomena, with the exception of very severely restricted ones, e.g., laws describing the behavior of white rats in a Skinner box. The question cannot be settled, however, by appeal to this type of philosophizing. I want only to point out that there is no good reason to assume that, in all cases, there are macroscopic laws waiting, as it were, to be discovered, and some reason to suppose that there may, in some cases, be none.

We shall consider now the role of historical concepts in genetic analysis. Historical concepts as such, in the sense which I have explained, have no peculiar function in the pattern of genetic analysis. This can be seen if we consider that the requirement of genetic analysis consists in exhibiting E as the outcome of chains of causally related events. In order to call attention to a persistent or continuously changing feature in the interval included in two successive links, any reference to factors that occurred prior to that interval is evidently superfluous. This does not mean that historical concepts cannot be used in genetic analysis, but that they can be used only in so far as they are E-defined by reference to features of the system exhibited in the interval considered in the analysis.

Historical concepts find an application, however, in the generalization of genetic analyses. In brief, they permit, in some cases, the widest reliable generalization of instances of genetic analysis. This can be demonstrated both by considering the logical pattern of genetic analysis, and by reference to biological examples.

Genetic analysis refers to aspects of past events which are considered the beginner-events of causal chains. The beginner-events are of course themselves intermediate links in causal chains that extend further back in time; the selection of particular events as beginners in genetic analysis is ontologically, therefore, somewhat arbitrary. Methodologically, the choice of beginners is dictated by a number of factors. First, the beginner should not be too close to E in time; otherwise the analysis, although it might be logically unexceptionable, will have very little interest. Second, the beginners must be causally related to their subsequent links, although the form of the causal connection, i.e., the laws relating the events, need not be, and in general are not, known. It can be seen that in order to have a generalizable genetic analysis—that is to say, a mode of selection of beginner-events that invariably, or for the most part, under statable conditions, yields a chain eventuating in a link characterized by E—a principle which selects beginner-events on the basis of their place in a chain of events, rather than on the basis of "intrinsic" properties of the events, would be methodologically helpful when the causal relations of these intrinsic properties are poorly understood. This, as I understand it, is the role of classificatory historical concepts in genetic analysis. The genetic analysis relates the beginner-event to a subsequent event characterized by E; historical concepts, functioning as criteria guiding the effective selection of beginner-events, pick out just those types of events which are already links in types of more extensive causal chains.

The extension of the genetic analyses of aspects of an individual organism's ontogeny to a wider class of ontogenies well exemplifies these points. If the beginner-event of a genetic analysis is fertilization of an egg, in the simplest case a generalization over a relatively narrow class of ontogenies is effected by selecting the eggs, and therefore the beginner-event, in accordance with a historical concept, in this case, "egg of species A." This concept is not defined by reference to morphological properties of the egg, although, to be sure, its historical W-definition may have served to direct inquiry to the point where a perfectly adequate E-definition in terms of morphology is available. On the other hand, there is certainly no guarantee that, at any given stage of inquiry, a proposed morphological E-definition of "egg of species A" is extensionally identical with its historical W-definition. If not, any attempt to generalize an historical analysis on the basis of the E-definition will be inaccurate, and perhaps wildly so.

Further generalization of a genetic analysis may often be gained by substituting the names of taxa of higher rank for "species A." This is always shaky. In practice embryologists utilize a combination of historical and morphological or physiological criteria in generalizing genetic analyses; an example is afforded by the rules describing, say, the early development of macrolecithal vertebrate eggs.

When the beginner-event is a later stage in ontogeny, the selection is ordinarily made on historical grounds by virtue of the fact that the scope of embryological laws are restricted in reference to taxonomic groups, and every taxon represents a historical concept. When higher taxa are E-defined morphologically, in almost all cases the morphological properties selected are properties of adult individuals. There are many reasons for this, but one reason important in this connection is given by the fact, summarized in one of Von Baer's laws, that, on the whole, the earlier the developmental stage of an organism, the more closely does that organism resemble the corresponding stage of organisms in distinct taxa of higher and higher rank. This makes the properties of early developmental stages poor guides for the segregation of embryos into their appropriate taxa. Under these conditions the historical criterion of taxon membership assumes an importance in the effective classification of organisms that it does not have when one is dealing with the adult stages. To put the point another way, if the goal is to write laws connecting the earlier and later stages of ontogeny, morphological criteria for selecting the beginner-stages are very unreliable. Owing to the facts of embryogeny first clearly stated by Von Baer, any selection of morphological properties is likely to include members of distinct higher taxa, and beginner-events selected on this basis will begin a whole series of divergent chains of events, very few of which may eventuate in the later stage characterized by E. To select the appropriate beginner, one relies rather on the historical criterion of taxon membership.

ONTOGENETIC AND PHYLOGENETIC
EXPLANATIONS

Woodger sharply distinguishes genetic explanations within an ontogeny from genetic explanations of events, or characters of events, of an ontogeny by reference to facts of phylogeny. His position seems to be that of the former, in so far as they can be generalized, yield laws, and can thus be made the basis for ordinary causal explanation, but causal explanation limited to the relations of dependence between parts that are manifested in normal development.

Experimental interference with ontogeny gives physiological knowledge, which is capable of wider generalization.[14]

Phylogenetic explanations, on the other hand, are historical in the stricter sense.

> The evolutionary process, because it *is* serial and because it is accomplished in a genetic succession of increasingly different individuals, is *unique*. Every event is of course unique, and in that sense an individual organism considered as an event is unique. But in its case it was . . . a part of a rhythmical succession, and consequently we can compare one individual development with another, and can recognize the same mode of characterization by a number of events. But in the case of evolution we cannot do this. The series of changes which have characterized the total event that we call evolution have, so far as we know, only occurred once.[15]

The conclusion that phylogenetic explanations cannot be generalized because they describe unique series of changes is then drawn on this basis.[16]

There is an important difference between ontogenetic and phylogenetic explanations, but it seems to me that Woodger has not correctly pointed out the difference. His view rests on a non sequitur, namely, that from the uniqueness of evolution as a whole, one can conclude that every phylogeny is unique. This conclusion, which does not follow, is necessary to support the view that genetic analyses of phylogeny cannot be generalized. This point is of some importance: Woodger is led to conclude on these grounds that causal explanation of evolution is impossible, in particular, that theories of natural selection do not provide causal explanation.[17] It is safe to say that biological literature abounds with speculations and arguments that could be avoided through closer attention to the logic of phylogenetic explanation, and of the logical, and more obvious empirical, relations between phylogeny and ontogeny. I shall make a few remarks on these topics, especially as they apply to Haeckel's Biogenetic Law and to the phenomena of recapitulation. This will bring us into the question of the pattern of what I have called genetic explanations proper and enable us to see the relations be-

[14] Woodger, *Biological Principles,* pp. 394–95.
[15] *Ibid.,* p. 393.   [16] *Ibid.,* p. 394.   [17] *Ibid.,* pp. 398, 421.

tween genetic analysis, genetic explanation, and the use of model techniques.

The term 'phylogeny' is understood by biologists in two senses that are not ordinarily distinguished. If forced to give an explicit statement, most biologists would say that by a "phylogeny" they understand a history compounded of the histories of a class of organisms every member of which is the ancestor of some specifiable class of organisms. In practice, most biologists actually understand the term to mean the history of the changes (or persistence), including the branchings, of the morphological type or, occasionally, the ecological and other properties of the adult stages of a succession of organisms related to each other as ancestors of a specifiable class of organisms. Haeckel's Biogenetic Law (or slogan, as most investigators regard it nowadays)—that ontogeny recapitulates phylogeny —quite clearly uses the term in its latter sense, since, of course, he did not envisage ontogeny as a series of high-speed developments of increasing "amplitude," each followed by regression to the zygote stage. But this is inconsistent with Haeckel's further insistence that phylogeny is the mechanical cause of ontogeny, since a series of differences in adult morphology over a period of generations is not the kind of thing that can be a cause—at least on the traditional analysis of the concept of cause. It is true that Haeckel postulated a special faculty of protoplasm, the "mneme" of the nuclei of the germ cells, to account for recapitulation,[18] but the doctrine was widely accepted by adherents of more orthodox views. Garstang's somewhat cryptic counterslogan, that ontogeny creates phylogeny, does not, as we shall see, suffer from this confusion.

Failure to distinguish these senses of "phylogeny" has led many people to think that a reasonably good fossil sequence is a phylogeny.[19] The results of the identification have been on the whole unfortunate: it is one aspect of, and tends to reinforce, the overemphasis upon the adult stages of organisms in morphological studies and in genetics; and it has led directly to a rather curious view that crops up continuously in various guises, namely, that evolution proceeds

[18] Haeckel, *Evolution*, p. 78.
[19] For a contemporary example, see Gallie, "Explanations," *Mind*, LXIV, 166.

simultaneously on various levels, the levels being defined by the
characters of various taxonomic rank assigned to the adult organisms. A clear example is afforded by L. S. Berg's opinion that the
appearance of the "diagnostic characters" of higher-rank taxa in the
course of evolution is determined by law (nomogenesis), that their
appearance is due entirely to "internal (autonomic) causes inherent in the very nature of the organism, and independent of any
effects of the environment." This high-level evolution is paralleled
by local adaptations. "The laws of development of the organic world
are the same both in ontogeny and phylogeny." [20] A similar view of
phylogeny is involved in all other orthogenetic theories, i.e., theories
which postulate special forces or special kinds of evolution to account for the major trends of evolution shown by fossil lineages of
adult organisms.[21]

Those who see phylogeny as the modification of adult morphology
are also prone to see a type of continuity between succeeding generations which does not really exist; or, perhaps more accurately,
they are prone to interpret the continuity shown in fossil sequences
on the analogy of the kind of continuity exhibited in the developmental phenomena of ontogeny. To interpret phylogeny in this way
is not so much wrong as it is misleading: on the one hand the interpretation has, as a matter of historical fact, fostered uncritical ac-
ceptance of Haeckel's Biogenetic Law, together with pseudoexpla-
nations of the law such as Berg's, or Haeckel's own introduction of
the protoplasmic "mneme"; and on the other hand it has led to the
belief that both ontogenetic and phylogenetic historical explanations
of an ontogenetic event or state share the same logical pattern and
differ only in the kind of events mentioned in the *explanans*.

To make these points clearer, and to bring out the logical character of phylogenetic explanations—which differs significantly in
pattern from ontogenetic analysis—it will be necessary to examine
briefly the relation between ontogeny and phylogeny, and the relation of both to the systematic categories and taxa.

Every ontogeny is a developmental history that begins either with

[20] Berg, *Nomogenesis*, p. 170.
[21] For a critical analysis of the meaning of "levels" of evolution and the
relation between these levels and the ranks of the systematic hierarchy, see
Simpson, *Major Features*, pp. 338–50.

the fusion of two cells—the gametes—to form the zygote or, in the case of parthenogenetic reproduction, with the cleavage of an unfertilized female gamete. I shall say that a zygote is the "fusion-product" of either or both gametes that cooperate in its formation. If the adult organism produces gametes, each gamete stands in some power of the relation "daughter-cell of" to the beginner-cell of the ontogeny. Let us say that cell A is a "cell-descendant" of B if A stands to B in some power of the relation "either daughter-cell or fusion-product of."

We may now define "phylogeny" in terms of the converse of the cell-descendant relation. The phylogeny of a class K of organisms (which may be a taxon, a cross-taxon category such as "fish" or "dinosaur," or a unit class) is the succession of all ontogenies whose beginner-cells stand in the converse of the cell-descendant relation to the beginner-cells of the ontogenies in K. When biologists speak of a phylogeny, they ordinarily mean a segment of a phylogeny as here defined, that is, a succession of ontogenies occupying a prescribed time interval. And of course, in most cases, the biologist is not interested in all the ontogenies in a phylogeny, but, as a rule, only in phylogenetic lines and in the time of occurrence and characteristics of ontogenies at points where two or more lines join. By a "phylogenetic line" within a phylogeny of K, I understand the phylogeny of any subclass of K. Thus when a paleontologist speaks, for example, of the phylogeny of the mesozoic reptiles, he explicitly sets upper and lower limits on the time interval he is considering; moreover, he is no doubt thinking in terms of a number of lines defined by the taxa included in the taxon "reptilia"; if he is interested in the broad view, the lines will probably be defined by orders; if in a finer view, by families, genera, or even species.

The reader will notice that the definition makes the phylogeny of K identical with the succession of all the ancestors of the members of K. The reason for the slightly more complicated definition is simply to call attention to the well-known logical and empirical relations between phylogenies and ontogenies and to emphasize what is involved in phylogenetic change and continuity. In order to speak intelligibly of *a* phylogenetic change, it is necessary to define K in such a way that it is sufficiently narrow for every line, or at least

most of the lines, defined by subclasses of K, to exhibit the change
in question. Now I am tempted to say that what really changes in
the course of a phylogeny is the type of ontogenetic development,
but, of course, many other things change as well: the properties of
the adult organisms in the succession, their mode of reproduction,
the probability of finding a given allele at a given locus, etc. Nevertheless, there is good reason, from the biologist's point of view, to
regard the change in type of individual development as fundamental, for it is in development that the organism acquires the properties designated by the term 'character'—all those dispositions,
structures, mechanisms, and attributes that enable the organism to
perform the functions of life. To have an adult character such as a
particular color is to possess a type of development that eventuates
in an organism with that color. A number of writers have pointed
out this fact, which, in spite of its obviousness, has often been ignored in favor of the uncritical assumption that adult characters as
such are the "effect" of "causes" present in the germ. Woodger points
out in detail the unhappy methodological consequences that have
flowed from the latter assumption.[22]

There are two practical alternatives to viewing phylogenetic
change as change in type of development: one, which I have already
discussed, is to view it as change in adult type; the other is to view
it as change in frequencies of genes found at various cuts in a phylogenetic line. A number of geneticists nominally favor this view,[23]
although in practice they do not take it seriously. Exclusive attention
to either of these changes in a phylogeny would cut the biologist off
from considering factors that are fundamental in evolution: the
former view suggests that only adult organisms are subjected to selection; the latter fails to relate change in any way to adaptation.
The essence of evolution is the differential frequency of inclusion
of different types of ontogenies in a phylogenetic line; the selection
is determined by the interrelations of environmental factors with the
developing organism.

In the light of these facts, is it possible to regard phylogenetic ex-

[22] Woodger, *Biological Principles*, pp. 334–61.
[23] Dobzhansky, *Genetics*, p. 11; and Wright, "Statistical Consequences," in
New Systematics, ed. Huxley, p. 164.

planations as a special application of the pattern of genetic analysis? We may distinguish two cases: phylogenetic explanation of a property of an organism, e.g., the path of the artery in Woodger's example; and phylogenetic explanation of a type of ontogenetic change.

In order to present a genetic analysis of a property of an organism, it is necessary to exhibit the property as the outcome of a continuous chain of events that are causally related. But the requirement of continuity is violated in phylogenetic explanation. There is certainly continuity in phylogenetic lines, but that continuity is not exhibited in the historical materials on which phylogenetic explanations are based. I am not referring to gaps in the fossil record. These are not, in principle, a logical obstacle to genetic analysis. The logical obstacle consists in the fact that the events we should call the adult stages of an organism are not contiguous with the corresponding events of preceding and succeeding generations. The continuity in a phylogenetic line is expressed in the definition of phylogeny: the zygote of every ontogeny is a cell-descendant of a large class of the zygotes in the phylogenetic line. There are no gaps in the cell-line. To regard a phylogenetic explanation as a special case of genetic analysis is really to hold the fantastic position that the same adult has undergone gradual modification in the course of evolution. There should be even less tendency to regard phylogenetic explanation of a whole ontogeny as a genetic analysis. The end of one event—the reaching of sexual maturity and the formation of gametes—is immediately succeeded by fertilization and the first stages of ontogeny. A whole ontogeny cannot immediately succeed another ontogeny.

In short, phylogenetic explanation must employ a general theory of heredity. It need not be a Mendelian theory, but in order to utilize the technique of genetic analysis, it requires the following elements: there are sets of factors in the zygote that determine, at least in part, the subsequent development of the zygote; some of these factors are present in the gametes, presumably having been inherited through the cell-line; [24] and the sets of factors in the zygote may

---

[24] Darwin's theory of pangenesis assumes that some of the factors in the gametes are carried there from the bodily organs by the blood. This doctrine is totally unnecessary in a purely selectionist theory of evolution, which Dar-

differ from those in the zygotes of its ancestors. We have here the logical conditions for a genetic analysis of the factors in a zygote, by inferring a continuous change, as we trace back the cell-line, on the basis, e.g., of fossil evidence. The beginner-events are a set of zygotes related to the zygotes of the ontogenies under analysis by some power of the converse of the cell-descendant relation; cell-divisions and fusions are the unit of analysis. Such genetic analysis does not itself yield a genetic explanation of a character or type of ontogeny. For this it is necessary and sufficient to relate sets of factors in the zygote with type of ontogenetic development. In practice, the set of factors is most often described in terms of the characters exhibited by the mature organism.

Phylogenetic explanation is a type of model-explanation. The field of the model consists of the ontogenies of the specimens under analysis and of the ontogenies of a selected class of the specimens' ancestors. The subject is the set of cell-lines that stretch continuously through the phylogeny and the factors inherited along the cell-lines. There are a number of simplifying assumptions. The factors are not enumerated; enough are assumed for the case at hand. It is supposed that any zygote at a temporal slice of the phylogeny is a fair sample of the other zygotes at that slice, and the rest are ignored, even though it is known that any of the class of zygotes may actually have made contributions to the zygote under analysis. The subsidiary hypotheses are the assumed laws connecting the course of ontogenetic development with the zygotic factors.

Phylogenetic explanation consists in a genetic analysis of the zygotic factors, coupled with Humean explanation of ontogenies in terms of the factors. The factors themselves are, of course, inferred entities; their character is specified functionally, in terms of the ontogenetic processes to which they contribute. It happens that there is independent evidence for the "reality" of the zygotic factors, namely, the behavior of the chromosomes at meiosis, and the elegant explanation this behavior affords for the laws of segregation

---

win's was not. As long as you give a zygote the power to "make" an adult, you might as well let that power be inherited through the cell-line, rather than have it gathered from the parts of the adult organism. The doctrine of pangenesis is a model for explaining the inheritance of "acquired characters," which Darwin believed to exist.

and independent assortment. Even here, there are writers who would insist that the factors—the genes—are not "things" in the common sense, but are hypothetical constructs. The question of the reality of the factors is of course irrelevant to the questions of the role of the factors in phylogenetic explanation. In fact, it is possible to interpret phylogenetic explanation as a model-technique which does not employ reference to hypothetical constructs, if one is willing to admit that genetic analysis is not an essential component in phylogenetic explanation. This interpretation may be illustrated in an example.

Suppose that an adult organism, a member of taxon T, has a morphological property P, and that if the phylogeny of the organism in a historical interval is divided into n subintervals, all, or most, members of the phylogeny in the subintervals will have had morphological properties F_1, F_2, . . . , F_n, where F_1 is the property in the earliest subinterval; F_2, the property in the succeeding subinterval, etc. Suppose also that no organism in the phylogeny with an F also has P. If every organism in T possesses a phylogeny with these characteristics, it is possible to write a general empirical hypothesis of the form, "If the members of the phylogeny of an organism O were characterized by F_1 at t_1, F_2 at t_2, . . . , F_n at t_n, then O will be characterized by P." This law is a nonmathematical analogue of a much more general "historical law" as described by Bergmann.[25] It might not be very general, although in all probability it would hold for all members of T if T is a species, whatever P and the F's might denote, since all the members of a species have the same ancestors, and hence the same phylogeny, if we ignore a few preceding generations. Such laws might be shown to hold for taxa of higher rank, even up to the phyla.

I shall say that any property or event E is genetically explained if its presence or occurrence is deducible from a set of statements $F_1(t_1)$, $F_2(t_2)$, . . . , $F_n(t_n)$ together with one or more laws of a form analogous to that of the above historical law, or if E is given a model-explanation with the help of subsidiary hypotheses connecting E with a set of hypothetical factors H and the constitution of

[25] Bergmann, "Problems of Psychology," in *Philosophy of Science*, ed. Feigl and Brodbeck, p. 634.

H is established by genetic analysis (aided in turn, perhaps, by simplifying assumptions and other subsidiary hypotheses). Either type of explanation would ordinarily be called "genetic" or "historical," and the definition distinguishes genetic analysis from genetic explanation in the Humean Pattern.

The question might arise that since both types of explanation can be applied to exactly the same empirical data ultimately there is no difference between them. We have a zygote before us; what difference does it make if we say that the zygote will yield an organism with P because it possesses a set of factors H, whose presence we infer solely on the basis of fossil evidence, rather than saying that it will yield an organism with P because its ancestors, as we infer from fossil evidence, had such and such properties? In other words, are we not always at liberty to say that any evidence we might gather that a historical event of a particular kind has taken place is to be taken as evidence for the presence of a hypothetical "trace" existing in the present? This is the problem of "mnemic causation." Most philosophers are opposed to the idea of mnemic causation on grounds that are partly epistemological and partly empirical. In the first place, it can never be proved that mnemic causation actually occurs; and secondly, working on the assumption that mnemic causation does not occur has been on the whole successful. Accordingly, most philosophers, and most scientists as well, would regard historical laws as in principle eliminable from a theory. I agree with this view. But it should be noticed that elimination of a historical law involves the fulfillment of two conditions. Laws must be found with equal or greater explanatory power; and, although historical evidence may be relevant in determining the presence of inferred conditions and the values of variables, these conditions and variables must not be W-defined historically. To use Bergmann's example, it might be easier to determine the state of food deprivation by timing a period of starvation than by a physiological test carried out in the present.[26] But if it is logically impossible, e.g., for a rat to be in a certain state without having had a certain history, any contemporary evidence that it is in that state is evidence for the occurrence of historical events, and any law which utilizes reference to the

[26] *Ibid.*

state is a historical law. This point illustrates the relation between historical concepts and genetic explanations. In so far as a hypothetical construct is W-defined, e.g., by a history of reinforcement, explanation in terms of the construct is historical explanation.

An instructive example of a historical law is afforded by a well-known genetic phenomenon.[27] Suppose that members of two plant species A and B, where A and B are of distinct genera, are crossed, and that the offspring C form seeds, some of which are viable and yield a third generation, D. The law can be stated as follows: crosses within D are normally fertile; but crosses between A and D or B and D are either totally infertile or else very reduced in fertility. Notice that the class D is W-defined historically. A and B are taxa and are also historical, but that is not the point here. We have a genuine historical law ascribing to the members of a historically defined class a nonhistorical relation with members of its ancestral species. The genetic mechanism involved is well understood: the F_1 generation forms a few diploid gametes, and their fertilization yields a tetraploid zygote. These plants then form diploid gametes which, when fertilized by the haploid gametes of the ancestral forms, produce zygotes suffering from "genic imbalance," and whose chromosome will segregate anomalously at cleavage. Organisms like those in C with respect to ancestry are known as "allotetraploids"; this too is a historical concept. In this case it seems to me possible in principle to rewrite the law after eliminating all historical concepts, but it would require more delicate experimental techniques than are now available. An effective way of identifying tetraploids, and the types of chromosomes they contain, without reference to historical data, would have to be worked out.

THE USE OF HISTORICAL EXPLANATION

Scientists are most likely to have recourse to historical explanation, not merely when the present phenomena are explicable in terms of past data, since this is true for many nonhistorical explanations, but also when present phenomena seem explicable in terms of a temporal sequence of past events. The regular connection is found

[27] The account is adapted from Darlington, "Taxonomic Species," in *New Systematics*, ed. Huxley, p. 142.

to hold, not between a past and a present event, but between a series of past events, occurring in a regular order, and the present event. It is under these conditions that the more speculative scientists have invoked in matter a mnemic function. It seemed, for example, to Haeckel that the unicellular radiolaria which he studied could construct their delicate and complex tests only if they "remembered" the necessary sequence of activities employed by their ancestors.[28] Haeckel and others applied the same concept in an attempt to understand the phenomena of recapitulation.

The significance of recapitulation, i.e., how it is to be explained, has been a fertile ground for controversy which has always involved at least some consideration of the logic of historical explanation. The reason for this is plain: as soon as the existence of recapitulatory phenomena was recognized, it was seen that what happened in phylogeny was not merely relevant to what happens in ontogeny, but that the sequence of events in phylogeny in some sense determines the sequence of events in ontogeny. The difficulties in the way of a straightforward analysis of the situation into causes and effects, as conceived by Hume, should be recognized. There is no prima facie constant conjunction of A-like and B-like events in recapitulation, but a parallelism of sequences of events that occur at times which may be separated by geological time intervals.

We have noted Berg's treatment of recapitulation, and the confusions that underlay it. He held the sublimely simple, though untenable, view that ontogeny and phylogeny are governed by the same laws. Haeckel held that whatever laws regulate phylogeny (he was in fact a selectionist) the germ "remembers" what happened in phylogeny, and performs it again at an accelerated pace, with perhaps another stage or two superadded at the end. De Beer has devoted considerable writing to refuting this view, largely through the gathering of empirical material on ontogenetic phenomena which do not exhibit recapitulation.[29] Perhaps it should be said that, from the side of methodology, Haeckel's thesis can be made to look less mystical and can achieve an equivalent result, if it is held merely that the germ "remembers" the ontogeny of its parents, repeats it

[28] Haeckel, *Evolution*, pp. 77–78.
[29] De Beer, *Embryology and Evolution*.

at approximately the same rate, and may add a stage or two. It logically follows that ontogeny will recapitulate phylogeny in the sense in which Haeckel understood the latter term. His statement that phylogeny is the mechanical cause of ontogeny can then be interpreted to mean that the factors which brought about added stages in the past are the cause of stages earlier in ontogeny in the present.

Haeckel's Biogenetic Law encountered difficulty from the first, not through methodological analysis, but through intractable empirical data, namely, that the early stages of ontogeny do not at all resemble the adults of the ancestors, and that there are many types of foetal adaptations, e.g., birth membranes. De Beer points out cases of heterochrony, i.e., reversal in the order of appearance of organs in ontogeny as against their phylogenetic order.[30] However, it is universally acknowledged that there are, in ontogeny, cases of genuine recapitulation: T. H. Morgan gives as especially clear examples in mammals the formation of nonfunctional yolk sacs and the appearance of the Graafian follicle.[31] The problem is to specify in what sense phylogeny explains recapitulation phenomena in ontogeny.

I interpret phylogenetic explanation as genetic explanation by genetic analysis coupled with a model. The model is in fact employed by embryologists; I shall illustrate it with a concrete application due to Julian Huxley.

In the model we assume the well-established hypotheses of genetics in toto. Assume further that genes can begin to exert their effects on ontogeny at any stage of development. Since mutations are random, a large proportion of mutant genes will have deleterious effects, and the earlier such genes begin to exert their effects, the more deleterious they are likely to be, due to the "magnifying effect" of development. Accordingly, genes which begin their work late in development have the greater probability of spreading throughout a population. The broad facts of recapitulation follow: phylogenetic divergence will manifest itself most markedly in the later ontogenetic stages.

The model provides a schema for approaching specific recapitulatory phenomena through genetic analysis (in my sense) of the

[30] *Ibid.*, p. 24.   [31] T. H. Morgan, *Embryology and Genetics*, pp. 56–57.

continuous phylogenetic cell-lines. It also provides for the exceptions such as foetal adaptations, larval adaptations accompanied by metamorphosis, and effects such as heterochrony. The model functions in the direction of research into the details of developmental physiology, and it also provides considerable grounds for inference concerning the taxonomic affinities and probable ancestors of living forms.

Huxley applies the model to a case of recapitulation shown in the gibbons.

> We find that the relatively long-armed Gibbons have a fetus which, though longer-armed than that of the other anthropoids, is relatively shorter-armed than the adult. . . . Presumably the line of least biological resistance in altering proportions of limbs, etc., is to modify relative growth rates, rather than to modify the original partition of material in the early embryo between organ and rest-of-body. And if this is so, the recapitulatory phenomenon follows automatically.[32]

This explanation involves both a genetic analysis—tracing the inheritance of a block of genes from the shorter-armed ancestor to the gibbons, which are assumed to regulate the whole ontogeny of the ancestral form with respect to the apportionment of materials in the arms and body—and the postulating of a later-acting gene that modifies the relative growth-rate of arms and bodies. This is a necessary subsidiary hypothesis.

Genetic explanations are "sufficiency" explanations, but in general they are not predictive. This is due to their model character. In the model, just those subsidiary hypotheses are assumed that will enable the deduction of the *explanandum*. Often, as in Huxley's example, there is no independent evidence that the subsidiary hypotheses are indeed exemplified in the system: no one knows whether or not the growth-constant [33] of the body-limb ratio in gibbons was altered by a mutation. But of course the existence of the *explanandum* is some evidence for the truth of the *explanans,* especially if it can be shown that the applicability of the subsidiary hypotheses is not anteced-

[32] Huxley, *Relative Growth,* pp. 234–35.
[33] The general formula for relative (heterogonic or allometric) growth is $\log y = \log a + b \log x$, where a is a constant of proportionality, and b is a constant, the growth-constant, whose value varies from system to system.

ently improbable. The law of allometric growth is known to be applicable to some systems, and it is known that the growth-constant can be altered by mutations. Huxley's model consists in extending the scope of the allometric law and making the simplifying assumption that the growth-constant was altered some time in the past.

Genetic analyses, on the other hand, do not pretend to be sufficiency explanations, although they can be easily converted into genetic explanations by the use of a model, i.e., by the introduction of subsidiary hypotheses and simplifying assumptions. An important accessory device, in the construction of both genetic analyses and explanations, is the use of historical concepts. To my knowledge, this topic has never been investigated. Without doubt, there are aspects of the use of historical concepts in genetic explanations which I have overlooked, but it seems plausible to me that their chief function is to provide rules for the formation of concepts that will group systems together on the basis of their possession of "lower-level" properties that determine the behavior of the systems, but which are poorly described. The use of historical concepts is thus inseparable from the problem of organization. The historical definitions of classes of zygotes, embryos—in general, of the taxa of various ranks, and concepts such as "hybrid" and "polyploid" are cases in point. We shall subsequently discover an analogous use for functional concepts.

CHAPTER VI

Functional Analysis

The complex of questions that pass under the name of "the problem of teleology" constitute without doubt one of the most confused parts of biological methodology. There is one fundamental reason for this: the philosophical critics of teleology and its defenders from the side of biological theory have consistently worked at cross-purposes. I shall not say that philosophers attack a straw-man teleology, but the doctrines that are most often criticized are of a type that few scientists, including most of the organismic biologists, would care to defend. It is not my purpose to approach these problems through an analysis of these criticisms, and what they accomplish or fail to accomplish, but as an example, we may notice the point, often made in a variety of ways, that the end of a goal-directed process is not an efficient cause of the process. The point is no doubt true, but few people have believed this doctrine. Aristotle, of course, distinguishes efficient from final causes, and not even Driesch thought that entelechies were efficient causes. Some philosophers seem to believe (since they change the subject at this point) that this observation suffices to show teleological explanation as misdirected and unscientific. But the premise on which the inference is based—that any factors that are not efficient causes have no place in science—cannot bear the light of explicit formulation.

On the other hand, the biological defenders of teleology cannot be said to have proved their point. R. S. Lillie, W. E. Agar, and E. S. Russell, perhaps the most explicit defenders among the organismic biologists, have not, to my knowledge, offered a clear formulation of the logic of their position. Agar and Russell present a wealth of empirical material to illustrate their points, but it is not shown unequivocally that the material illustrates their own views and is incompatible with the views of their opponents. The upshot is a good deal of biology, interesting and suggestive, but, from the philosophical point of view, exasperatingly inconclusive. One example will suffice as illustration. Organismic biologists have seen a deadly foe in the theory or tropisms or forced-movements associated with the name of Loeb. Agar offers an analysis of an experiment in criticism of the theory. The forced-movement theory assumes that insects which are positively phototropic move toward the light because the differential illumination of their eyes sets up differential frequencies of neural impulses, which in turn causes faster, or more energetic, contraction of the leg muscles of one side. But, objects Agar, the same insect may show the same behavior if two legs on one side are amputated: the insect will turn toward the light by suitable adjustments of the motions of his remaining legs. This phenomenon is said to indicate that the behavior is goal-directed, and not merely a forced-movement.[1]

One can grant that this experiment (and any number of similar ones) shows that the expression "forced-movement" is ill-chosen. But it does not prima facie refute the theory of tropisms; it is only necessary to assume a rather more complicated internal mechanism. If Agar had clearly stated what counts as evidence for goal-directed activity, or against the tropism theory, this objection need not have arisen.

In the present and succeeding chapter I shall attempt to make explicit what is of scientific value in the teleological point of view. I shall examine the logical character of teleological language; offer an explication of the term 'teleological system'; and apply the explication to an analysis of teleological explanation. The first task will occupy this chapter; it seems to me the most neglected, whereas there is a considerable literature, whose results I shall utilize, on the second two topics. I consider that the best way to show that much criticism of teleology is misplaced will be to present a positive account of the logical function of teleological language. Subsequently I shall maintain that this account renders defensible a particular interpretation of the organismic biologist's position on teleology, and shows how the empirical material discussed by them does illustrate their position. The alleged differences between "mechanism" and "teleology," or between causal- and order-

---

[1] Agar, *Living Organism*, p. 117.

analytical propositions do not, however, provide us with the tools for this analysis.

FUNCTION AND MORPHOLOGY

The discussion of teleology will be facilitated by a distinction between two types of teleological "explanation." The distinction is roughly this: on the one hand we often find biologists describing the function of particular parts of an organism, e.g., the liver or the chloroplasts, and of organic processes and mechanisms, e.g., regeneration and sexual reproduction. This is sometimes called "teleological" or "functional explanation." Nagel gives as an example of such explanations, "The function of chlorophyll in plants is to enable plants to perform photosynthesis." He correctly points out that biologists who speak in this way "are not necessarily committing the pathetic fallacy or lapsing into anthropomorphism." [2] Statements of this form, and others of more or less similar form, abound in biological writings, and certainly do not presuppose a theory of final causation. Nagel states that some confusion would be avoided if the term "teleological" were not used here.[3] I think that other confusions could be avoided if the term 'explanation' were also abolished in these contexts. For notice that nothing corresponding to an *explanans* and *explanandum* are distinguishable within the statement. Only the most Palaeozoic reactionary would maintain that "Plants have chlorophyll" is explained by "Plants perform photosynthesis." In any case, there is nothing in the statement that remotely resembles explanation in the Humean Pattern. Accordingly, I shall call statements that ascribe functions to a part, process, etc., "functional analyses." [4] The language employed in functional analysis will be considered in the present chapter.

On the other hand, we find biologists employing full-fledged teleological explanations, which do meet the stringent logical requirements of the Humean Pattern. A full examination of the logic of these explanations will require a preliminary examination of teleo-

[2] Nagel, "Teleological Explanation," in *Philosophy of Science,* ed. Feigl and Brodbeck, p. 541.
[3] *Ibid.*
[4] Nagel uses the term "teleological analysis" to refer to the process of inquiry into such functions. *Ibid.,* p. 540.

logical systems and behavior. For the present they may be defined as "sufficiency" model-explanations which employ in the *explanans* some reference to the goal-state of the *explanandum*, i.e., of a process, action, etc., which is objectively goal-directed. If one grants that there are such explanations, it will be granted that they should be distinguished from functional analyses.

The two major aspects of teleological language, including functional analyses, employed in the biological sciences which will be examined are expressed in the following questions: (1) What functions do teleological propositions actually perform in biological theory? Could they be eliminated without loss from the language of biology? (2) Are there concepts, as distinct from propositions, whose employment commits the user to teleological language? If so, what is the logical character and function of these concepts, and could they too be eliminated without loss from biological language? It must be admitted that both purges have been strongly recommended by numerous writers. I shall maintain that the far-reaching implications of such purges have not been fully recognized. The essence of my position is that teleological language is really quite innocent of the crimes of which it is suspected, and is in fact an indispensable tool in morphology, ethology, and evolution theory.

A functional analysis attributes to a part or process a role in the performance of some activity. To give a functional analysis of a system s or a process F is to say that there is a system s' and process F' (other than s and F) such that there is an environment in which s' exhibits F' if s is part of s' or that environment, or if F occurs, and in which s' would not exhibit F' if s were not part of s' or the environment, or if F failed to occur. This definition closely parallels the earlier definition of "functional concept"; the difference lies in the possibility that in functional analysis one may attribute to a part or process of kind K a function that it has as a matter of fact, and not as a matter of definition of K. For reasons to be stated later, I do not believe that in functonal analysis one states that the part or process is a necessary condition of the performance of the function.

By a "teleological concept" I shall understand a functional concept. My definition of the latter admittedly constitutes a reconstruction of "teleological concept" as the term is employed by other writers. However, it seems to me that the definition renders the sense of the expression as it is actually used, and that it serves to group together a class of concepts of great interest in the analysis of teleology. In the class we find obviously teleological concepts such as "tool," "organ," and "goal-directed," but it includes also a great number of concepts not usually regarded as teleological. It is through an examination of these "hidden" functional concepts that some of the significant logical features of teleological language may be brought to light. I shall examine their use and discuss their relation to functional analysis, especially in the fields of morphology and ethology.

One might expect that morphology would be the branch of biology in which functional analysis and the employment of functional concepts would be least likely to be found. Nevertheless, functional concepts (which presuppose prior functional analysis) are often used in "pure" morphological description. Morphology is not merely description of the spatial relations of physical parts; or, to put the point in a more accurate and a more suggestive form: morphological description requires the employment of descriptive concepts whose extensions are physical parts. But while the meaning of "physical parts" is perhaps exhaustively specifiable in terms of the concepts of "mass" and "spatial relation," the concept "physical part" is not itself employed in morphological description. Concepts such as "kidney," "femur," "trochanter," "Wolffian duct," "vagus nerve," "gill raker," etc., are employed in morphological descriptions. Kidneys and so forth are physical objects, but the concepts are not physical concepts. Failure to draw this elementary distinction gives rise to a completely erroneous view of the nature of morphology, and positively stands in the way of recognizing the extent to which functional analysis is involved in this most "static" part of biological theory. The view, which I regard as erroneous, consists in thinking that the concepts of "structure" and "form" are adequate for a definition of morphology and its branches anatomy, histology, and cytology. It consists in thinking that morphological concepts are defined in terms of the visible features—color, shape, position, etc.—which reveal themselves in the single organism that the dissector or microscopist has before him. Morphology is considered a "foundation" of biology, a necessary but nontheoretical hack work similar to patching together a map of a region out of aerial photographs before sending in serious explorers. The dictionary definition of morphology—"The branch of biology dealing with the form and structure of animals and plants" [5]—embodies the view. A contemporary biologist expresses it in the following passage:

The enormous multiplicity exhibited by living things necessitates at the outset a description of the visible "characters" of particular organisms— their forms, proportions, colors, and measurable magnitudes. This morphological description relates not only to the external, but also, in the form of anatomy, to the internal, structures, the construction and mutual spatial relations of the organs.[6]

It is as if the morphologist were given a task like the commercial artist commissioned to draw an accurate representation of a large piece of electronic equipment, except that the morphologist must rely more heavily on words. But if we closely examine the language he does use, we see that the morphologist is much more like the engineer commissioned to draw a schematic diagram of the device's circuits. The morphologist's concepts correspond to the conventional symbols for switches, capacitors, relays, etc.; the indication of spatial relations corresponds to the diagram's indication of the circuit hookup. Electronic symbols are chosen in such a way that the skilled reader can infer, with the aid of theory, as many as possible of the behavioral characteristics of the circuit. And the morphologist chooses his concepts in order that his descriptions convey as much as possible of the workings of the organism being described. Physiology is the theory that mediates these inferences, and physiology is the theory which must inform the building of morphological concepts.

Now even if it is admitted that the concepts of morphology are not defined directly in terms of physical features of the single organism, it would not follow that they are functional concepts in my sense. Many writers would be willing to hold that the concepts of morphology, or at any rate part of them, are essentially comparative, or involve some reference to physiology. But I am maintaining more

[5] *Webster's Collegiate Dictionary* (5th ed.), p. 649.
[6] Mainx, *Foundations of Biology*, p. 8.

than the obvious point that morphological concepts are defined only after some investigation of different types of organisms, and after physiological considerations are taken into account. This could mean no more than, e.g., defining the concept in such a way that it is applicable across various taxa, and in fact refers to a structure that acts as a unit physiologically, i.e., to use a trivial case, to a whole muscle rather than to a segment of one. The position is rather that morphological concepts are physiological because they are comparative, and that adequate comparative concepts, that is, concepts which are applicable over a wide range of taxa, especially taxa of the higher ranks, in some cases can only be, and in many cases can most easily be, defined by reference to the role the structures play in the organism's physiology and in its gross behavior.

Suppose that one attempts to define a structure, the kidney, for example, by describing its shape, appearance, internal structure, etc. The definition cannot be so precise that it would arbitrarily rule out of the class of kidneys organs that have a shape like the required one, but, through normal variation, deviate from it. It cannot arbitrarily rule out abnormal kidneys. And it must be general enough to include not only the kidneys of such diverse organisms as mammals, and fish, but various invertebrates as well. It is apparent that what one ordinarily thinks of as a morphological description, i.e., in terms of colors and shapes, cannot be a definitive description of the kidney. A much closer approach to such a definition may be achieved if general bodily position of the organ and the paths of its ducts are taken into account. Here one would have to beware of eventually circular definition, for instance defining "kidney" in terms of "abdomen" and defining "abdomen" in terms of the organs it contains. In practice, a functional definition is the obvious way out. Any structure is said to be a kidney only if it contributes to a function F′, in this case excretion.

Notice that any concept which is W-defined in terms of a functional concept is itself functional. This consideration suggests that functional concepts may be very widespread indeed in morphology. Of course, the only way to discover their extent would be to conduct a rather thorough investigation of morphological theory, and of the way in which its concepts are actually employed. This is made difficult because morphologists do not write down definitions of their concepts. To commit oneself to a definition of concepts under these circumstances always involves an element of reconstruction.

The whole point may be put in the following way. An organism cannot be completely described; there are logical objections to the notion of complete descriptions, and in any case, no one would possess the time or patience. Only certain attributes of an organism are selected for description in morphology. Moreover, any organism is subject to a "conceptual" decomposition into parts in any number of distinct ways, again depending upon the concepts utilized in the analysis. My position is that any set of concepts W-defined by reference to visible shapes, colors, and spatial relations is applicable only to a very narrowly restricted class of organisms, and is therefore of limited value for the purposes of comparative morphology, physiology (including developmental physiology), and the description of phylogenetic changes. The use of functional W-definition does not guarantee a wider scope to the concepts of morphology, but evolution theory provides good grounds for supposing that concepts based on function will be more widely applicable than those based on structural properties. Structure is radical and function conservative in the economy of evolving organisms.

To say that a morphological concept is W-defined functionally is not to say that the biologist must make a physiological investigation each time he applies one. Indeed, it is essential that the concepts be regularly, even for the most part, applicable to dead organisms. This is accomplished by E-definition in terms of structural properties. Structural properties are very likely to be conservative within the species of a genus, somewhat less likely to be so within the genera of a family, and so on with each set of taxa included in a taxon of next higher rank. E_k-definitions with respect to taxa, and some cross-taxon groups can and must be achieved in terms of these structural properties. But an E_k-definition which is reliable for a class K may not be reliable for the class of organisms which in fact possess the structure in question. The functional definition makes E_k-definitions of the same concept in different terms logically possible, but more importantly, it embodies the information that guides the morphologist in his construction of E-definitions. The development of morphological concepts is a gradual process, in which more and more adequate formulations emerge from the interplay of the results of physiological investigations and from the study of the structural features of organisms. Functional analysis is an essential component of the interplay.

Morphological concepts are polytypic, and may be fully polytypic, with respect to structural and spatial properties, that is, with respect to those properties which are usually called morphological!

The problem of finding fruitful morphological concepts is one aspect of the problem of organization. The organism may be "conceptually" decomposed into parts in an indefinite number of ways. The morphologist has to find concepts that refer to those parts of the organism which, so to speak, represent the "natural" cleavages at a high level of organization—in fact, which represent just those cleavages that mark the parts of wide theoretical interest. There is no a priori way to decide upon the policy that would best accomplish this task. In practice, it turns out that the best policy is to select parts that act as a functional unit, i.e., the largest masses of substance, separated from other such masses, that contribute to a function. As a further point of practice, a relatively small number of functions are found to provide the necessary W-defining basis, e.g., locomotion, respiration, etc.

Morphology may be compared with systematics. The problem in both cases is to find concepts that group together systems of the widest interest from the point of view of particular biological theories. In both cases, functional concepts yield results that are most useful in evolution theory. It is a cardinal matter of economy that all morphological concepts should not be restricted to a particular species or other lower-rank taxon (although for various special reasons morphologists do introduce such concepts). To define morphological concepts by reference to structural properties is to run the risk of restricting their applicability so narrowly that it becomes virtually impossible to formulate laws concerning morphological parts, e.g., laws describing the evolutionary changes in form or function of a part, whose scope extends beyond a species or a few of the taxa which include it.

If we consider functional concepts and functional analysis in the field of animal behavior, further aspects of their use may be brought to light. E. S. Russell, who is noted for his insistence upon the necessity of teleological methods in this field, claims that these methods do not yield a knowledge of causal relations,[7] and asserts that such knowledge is in any case insufficient. He says that recognition of the goal-directed character of behavior is independent of knowledge of the causes of the behavior, but that it is absolutely necessary for "understanding" it, for making it "intelligible." [8]

Two comments may be made at this point. If (to use Russell's example) a wasp uses the wood pulp it chews from a fence post for building its nest, then that is a fact and therefore the business of the biologist to know. No one would deny this. Amateurs and professionals alike have enthusiastically investigated these matters and a thousand others like them. What more does Russell intend? He certainly does not intend the bare tautology that "understanding" consists in knowledge of such facts, and therefore we must know them in order to understand behavior. Does this view then reduce to a variation on the *verstehen* theme, that we fully understand an animal's behavior only when we can sympathize with it on the basis of its analogy with our own conscious purposes? This would not be Russell's view, but he nowhere offers a clear alternative. I shall try to provide one.

To give a functional analysis of a behavior-segment, e.g., a wasp chewing a fence post, a stickleback dancing before a female, a spider spinning a web, etc., is to do two things: (1) it is to select a level of analysis of the total behavior of the animal; and (2) it is to attribute more to the observed segment than is (logically) observable at the time the behavior takes place. Neither of these aspects of teleological analysis is peculiar to it; all scientific enquiry involves the prior selection of a level of analysis, and many scientific concepts involve the assignment of properties to a particular which are not observable at the time of predication. The logical significance of

---

[7] Russell, *Behaviour of Animals*, pp. 12–13, 15.   [8] *Ibid.*, p. 15.

functional analysis does not, accordingly, lie in a *sui generis* feature, but this does not detract from its usefulness.

The selection of a level of analysis is a distinguishable aspect of the total development of a theory. One does not select the level, and then proceed to form concepts and principles. Rather, the formation of concepts is controlled by their use in description and explanation, and this *involves* the selection of a level of analysis. The problem facing the ethologist may be compared to the problem facing the physiologist. The physiologist finds before him a particular object, the organism, of bewildering complexity. The concept of complexity is insufficiently analyzed, perhaps. In any case complexity is not merely a function of the ontological makeup of a system, but a function of this together with the conceptual tools with which we approach the system. The same system can be very simple when seen from one point of view, very complex when seen from another. The degree of complexity depends upon the availability of suitable concepts and laws for describing the aspects of the system that interest us. The organism is complex because those concepts which we have developed, and have found useful in describing organisms, define parts and processes, e.g., cells, tissues, chromosomes, organs; mitoses, invaginations, hydrolysis reactions, etc., which the organism, as a matter of fact, exhibits in great profusion. The behavior of animals presents a similar complexity. A relatively short segment of the behavior of a wasp is enormously complex if it is analyzed, say, into a series of limb movements, or of muscular contractions, or of short local displacements. This complexity in itself renders the task of explaining the units difficult, for there are many types, e.g., of limb movements, and they take place at different rates and in various orders. Such analysis is, of course, not impossible either in principle or in practice, but ethologists have in most cases selected units of behavior on an entirely different level. We may distinguish two general alternative approaches to the description of behavior, within each of which there are alternative levels of analysis. The first describes behavior as motion in relation to a geometrical background. This is the general method of description in the physical sciences. A coordinate system, which may be attached to the organism, or to the environment, may be established, and motions described in relation to it. The second is to describe behavior in terms of environmental objects manipulated, things accomplished, and things left undone. This distinction seems to me of great importance, not only for understanding the logic of functional analysis, but also for understanding the logical character of many of the concepts employed in learning theory.

In order to avoid a possible misunderstanding, I should point out that I recognize a certain difficulty in the distinction. Any segment of behavior involving, and describable as, a local motion of a whole organism or its parts in a trivial sense also "accomplishes" something, namely, that local motion. Conversely, whenever a segment of behavior accomplishes, e.g., escape from a predator, construction of a nest, etc., the behavior involves local motion of the organism or its parts and could be described as such. This is part of what is meant by saying that the same behavior may be analyzed at different levels. We must distinguish between the concepts used in the description of behavior and the behavior itself. To describe behavior in terms of objects manipulated, things accomplished and left undone, is to commit oneself to a set of concepts defined in terms of environmental objects, e.g., predators, food, building materials, wind currents, females, eggs, nests, etc., and actions performed "with respect to" environmental objects, e.g., escape, seeking, finding, avoiding, using, courting, protecting, warning, fighting, hiding, etc. By way of illustration, consider the behavior of a fish attacked by a shark: suppose that the fish wheels sharply and swims toward a reef, taking cover in a crevice in the rocks. The ethologist would apply the term "escape reaction" to this behavior. Notice that no combination of muscular movements, no series of local motions, no particular direction of movement, e.g., to the left or right, or away from the shark, is necessary for the application of the term "escape reaction." And obviously no feelings of fear, etc., are predicated of the fish. What is (logically) necessary is this: the behavior, whatever its character, must be such as to actually accomplish, in some environments, escape from danger, i.e., avoidance of a situation which would result in damage or death to the fish. Quite clearly, the concept "escape reaction" is a functional concept, and to apply the concept at all presupposes a prior functional analysis. To be sure, any number of the reactions of a fish might be such as to actually remove it from danger, but "escape reaction" is defined as a reaction which, under some environmental circumstances, accomplishes this.

Suppose now that it is objected that in the final analysis the concept of an escape reaction is after all superfluous, and might be altogether eliminated from biological theories. It might be suggested that we speak only of the response of "heading for the nearest rocks" to stimuli of such and such a kind. This preserves description in terms of environmental objects, but eliminates the functional concept. But we must ask how this reformulation would be accomplished, or better, how the nonfunctional formulation would be accomplished without the aid of the functional analysis. One would first have to identify "heading for the rocks" as a single response, not a chain of responses or an excised segment of a response, and then identify the stimuli. The latter task might be quite easy; the response may occur only when a shadow falls on the fish. (Even here, prior knowledge that the reaction is an escape reaction would indicate this as a strong possibility.) But it might be quite difficult, if the fish reacts to shapes of various kinds and to combinations of shapes and movements. It would be very helpful to know that the stimuli to be studied are those associated with predators.

None of these arguments are conclusive in favor of keeping the concept. One might grant these arguments, and still argue that knowledge of the function of responses is of great "heuristic value in the formation of hypotheses" (the formula comes readily to mind —one reads it so often), but this is no argument for the intrinsically teleological character of the concepts employed. This objection overlooks the point that the term 'escape reaction' is applied not only to the "heading for the rocks" response of this particular species, but to a great variety of responses characteristic of very different species as well. Heading for rocks, swimming toward open water, withdrawing into a shell, running for a burrow, zigzagging, gathering under the mother, etc., are all responses that are called "escape reactions." It would be very difficult to attempt to specify a set of characteristics, other than the functional one, which all these responses, and no others, possess. The class of escape reactions, to put it in other words, is fully polytypic with respect to those features of behavior observable in the single response, and with respect to movements in relation to any environmental coordinate system, e.g., movements toward or away from particular things. Accordingly, the functional concept accomplishes three things: (1) Its logical character permits a very wide application, providing a terminology for describing responses of very different behavioral appearance. (2) Its functional definition provides rules for effectively defining subclasses of escape reactions, e.g., those of the members of taxa of various rank, or all those occupying a particular ecological niche, in terms of their behavioral appearance. And (3) it segregates a class of responses which may show important uniform connections with other phenomena.

The last point is the most important and constitutes the final justification for the other two. There is of course no a priori reason why functionally defined classes should show regularities that classes which are not functionally defined do not. But in point of empirical fact, such concepts have proved most useful in the formulation of the most general ethological principles.[9] One is able to formulate important hypotheses with their aid, such as, "The escape reaction of every light sensitive dweller of the littoral bottom is released by a shadow," "Escape reactions are less subject to displacement to other functions than are mating reactions," and "The releasers of escape reactions may be changed by natural selection without change in the response pattern."

Not only do the functional concepts permit the formulation of these and similar hypotheses, but they indicate ways in which hypotheses of rather limited scope may be generalized. An example is afforded by the subsumption of a law connecting the appearance of a mating reaction with the lengthening of the day, and one connecting (other) mating reactions in other species to a change in mean temperature, under a single law connecting them with change in the size of the gonads, for which the lengthening day, the changing temperature, and perhaps many other factors, serve as stimuli in various taxa. Of course, it takes no great insight to see that there might well be a connection between gonad size and mating reaction; but that is exactly the point. Notice that both "gonad" and

[9] See especially Tinbergen, *Study of Instinct*, pp. 102–6.

"mating reaction" are functional concepts. Another obvious line of generalization is to describe the releasing stimuli of a functionally defined instinctive response in terms of functional concepts, e.g., to relate courtship responses to the appearance of females of the appropriate taxa, or to relate an "alarm reaction" to a "danger signal."

N. Tinbergen places great emphasis on the ethological problem of selection of an appropriate level of analysis. Although he does not utilize the concept of functional analysis, and is indeed critical of "teleology," he does employ functional analysis and functional concepts. He criticizes any attempt to analyze behavior at the level of muscular movements as being too fine-grained, and he criticizes K. S. Lashley for viewing such acts as mating as a single response. The former makes the writing of laws connecting stimuli and responses almost impossible to write; the latter makes the stimuli excessively complicated.[10] His own practice, which is typical in the respects under consideration of the approach of other ethologists, is illustrated in the treatment of the behavior of the stickleback, *Gasterosteus aculeatus*. He arranges the instinctive behavior of the fish in hierarchical form, the top level defined functionally as behavior promoting one of the major functions of the organism, e.g., reproduction. Reproductive behavior is divided into four categories: "fighting," "building," "mating," and "care of young." Each of these categories is defined by reference to objects manipulated or things accomplished. In addition, the last three concepts are clearly functional. Each of these behavior patterns is further divided into acts at the "consummatory" level, e.g., "care of young" includes "fanning (ventilating) the egg-clutch," "rescuing eggs," "removal of infected eggs." Each of these concepts is functional. The selection of these levels in the hierarchy enables Tinbergen to formulate a number of hypotheses, e.g., that no behavior at the consummatory level occurs in the absence of the drive-state associated with instinctive behavior at the top level of the hierarchy, and that the responses at the lower levels each possesses a relatively simple "releaser." He is able also to describe a hypothetical neural hierarchy affording a model-explanation of the behavior hierarchy.[11]

Another aspect of the same problem of levels is illustrated in the

[10] *Ibid.*, p. 51.   [11] *Ibid.*, pp. 103–4.

homologizing of instinctive animal behavior. The morphologist homologizes not cells or organ systems, but organs or parts of organs. On which level are we to search for behavior homologies? Tinbergen illustrates his answer with an example:

The two species [the sparrow-hawk and the long-tailed tit] both shape the cup of the nest by scraping. Solidity of the nest's wall, however, is brought about by different means: the sparrow-hawk makes quivering movements which are only weakly developed in the tit; the tit makes weaving movements which are not observed in the sparrow-hawk. Such a state of affairs leads us to the conclusion that we cannot simply say that nest-building is homologous in the two species. But it is possible to homologize parts of it, viz., the scraping movements. As these are found in many birds, . . . it is quite probable that homologization is justified. . . . Homologization is most profitable [therefore] when practiced at the level of behavior elements like scraping, quivering, etc.[12]

Why does Tinbergen homologize "scraping" and refuse to homologize "nest-building"? There are similarities in structure between any two cases of nest-building, and if it is possible that a segment of the behavior of nest-building of two species have a close common origin, nest-building as a whole could equally well have a close common origin. These are the two requirements for homologizing. And why not homologize limb motions or even muscle contractions? In the broadest sense, those behavior segments which can be homologized are those which (1) have their form determined by genetic factors other than the factors which influence the organism's anatomy and physiology; and (2) are released by a relatively simple stimulus. Thus the homologizing behavior segment is the unit of behavior that is directly subject to the pressures of natural selection and is thus of direct adaptive value. Nest-building as a whole is subject to natural selection, but only in an accidental sense, because natural selection "works" on the stimulus-response connection, and nest-building involves a chain of such connections. To regard nest-building as one response would require the postulation of an excessively complex stimulus stretching over a long period of time. Moreover, to find the stimuli that would allow the writing of simple laws connecting responses as analyzed at a different level with their stimuli would be a staggeringly difficult job, and then the

[12] *Ibid.*, pp. 190–91.

ethologist would face the task of "constructing" responses such as nest-building out of these responses. Thus there are methodological criteria of homology at the "level of homologous behavior segments"; this is the level on which the simplest laws may be formulated connecting stimuli with responses.

The discovery of homologies in behavior is accordingly facilitated by functional analysis. If one succeeds in analyzing behavior into functional segments, one has a way of describing behavior in respect of those properties which are indicative of degree of phylogenetic relationship, and which are most likely to be related to those aspects of the environment that the organism must deal with in order to prosper. Such segments can of course be described without the use of functional concepts—"quivering" is nonfunctional; but functional concepts avoid the risk of unnecessarily narrow specification.

We are now in a position to suggest a nontrivial interpretation of E. S. Russell's remark that until one knows the end served by a bit of behavior, one does not understand its "significance." I would suggest that this means simply that until a functional analysis of the behavior has been carried out, while we may be in a position to describe the single bit of behavior we have before us, we are not in a position to describe, with a set of uniform concepts, other behavior of the same animal on other occasions (e.g., behavior just like it with respect to types of stimuli and drive-state, but differing in any number of other respects, and in final issue—differences which are "insignificant" in the sense in which knowledge of the order in which I use the matches in a folder is insignificant for an understanding of my smoking habit); and we are also not in a position to describe types of behavior characteristic not only of this species but of broader classes which include it, e.g., taxa of higher rank, or categories defined ecologically. In short, without functional or teleological analysis, we cannot apply those concepts, and hypotheses constructed with their help, which would enable us to understand behavior in the ordinary sense of "understand."

I would not venture to guess whether this interpretation would please the organismic biologists, but it seems to me to include all that they can reasonably require in the way of "understanding."

The interpretation is certainly charitable. It changes the organismic biologist's thesis from a vague and at best doubtful thesis about the logical (or psychological) ground of "significance" into an empirical hypothesis about what policy is most likely to lead to a systematic theory of behavior, in the sense in which that term is understood by empiricists. Moreover, it is a hypothesis which the literature of ethology may be seen to support. No reference is made to a unique pattern of inquiry, and clearly there is no need to transcend the "causal-analytic" method. And most importantly, it assigns to functional analysis a role in the development of theory: the discovery of the functions served by a behavior segment (and by a morphological structure or physiological process) is not merely the addition of a new fact to the catalogue of science, although it is at least that.[13] In addition, these facts become the raw materials for the formation of functional concepts. Subsequently we shall see how the facts stated in functional analyses may be utilized in special types of teleological explanations.

The logical peculiarities of teleological language must be understood against this methodological background. Characteristically teleological phrases such as "seize an opportunity," "fail to escape," "seek for food," "explore strange places," "serve the purpose"; to "flee," "avoid," "strive," "enable," "permit," "prevent"; and "function," "goal," "end," owe their appropriateness in biology not to the fact that much organic behavior is directly adaptive in nature, but to the fact that so much of this behavior is fruitfully describable in the language of objective manipulation and of things accomplished. All functional analysis could be carried out without the aid of functional concepts, but the resulting theory would be a piecemeal affair. As soon as one finds reason for admitting into science a functional concept such as "food" or "distress signal," one might as well admit the rest of the teleological vocabulary, with the proviso that those locutions which either presuppose or strongly suggest the presence of consciously entertained ends-in-view may well be avoided. There is nothing intrinsically anthropomorphic in teleological language as such, although much anthropomorphic

---

[13] This seems to be the only function assigned to teleological analysis by Von Bertalanffy. Von Bertalanffy, *Modern Theories*, p. 10.

language is teleological. A teleological "ring" is built into the grammar of the language in which we describe achievement and failure. As soon as it is appropriate to speak of "food" and "hunting food," it is also appropriate to speak of failure to find it, opportunities missed in the search, redoubled efforts, distractions from the goal, fulfillment of the purpose, success. Such language is appropriate; I would not say that it cannot mislead, or as Von Bertalanffy holds, that it cannot be avoided.[14]

THE USES OF FUNCTIONAL ANALYSIS

It may be assumed that people who think that teleological language ought to be eliminated from science are disturbed by the spirit and not merely the letter of this language. The actual expressions are taken to indicate an underlying confusion, perhaps between function and cause, or between an outcome and a purpose; or they are thought to be anthropomorphic, or to presuppose an untenable metaphysics. Of course, no one would say that "Ant lions dig traps for their prey" or "Some animals amputate a limb in order to escape an attacker" are unverifiable or meaningless. It is maintained rather that such statements have a verifiable component, an asserted content, but also suggest an additional component. Two points of view, from the critical side, may be taken toward the additional component: (1) It may be argued that it is unverifiable; e.g., "Ant lions dig traps for their prey" asserts that ant lions dig traps, that animals do in fact fall into the holes, and that these animals may be eaten, but the formulation suggests that the ant lion digs his hole as a trap, with an end-in-view. (2) It may be maintained that a teleological statement is identical in meaning with a nonteleological paraphrase, and that the teleological statement serves to suggest that the system under consideration has properties which may not be exhibited in the behavior described in the statement, e.g., that the system is self-maintaining, or "directively organized." [15] This is my own position. But of course to show that a teleological statement can be translated into a nonteleological

---

[14] *Ibid.*, p. 9.
[15] Nagel, "Teleological Explanation," in *Philosophy of Science*, ed. Feigl and Brodbeck, p. 552.

one is not to recommend that such translations be carried out in practice. The important point is to see how the logical character of teleological formulations (which is preserved in the translation) aids in biological enquiry.

With respect to the former attitude, my own view is that philosophers have greatly overestimated the amount of illicit suggestions embodied in teleological formulations. No doubt some people are sometimes misled into unverifiable or even false attribution of psychic activity to organic systems, but the advantages of teleological expressions, for the reasons I have given, seem to me to far outweigh this disadvantage. If a critic insists upon seeing anthropomorphism in all teleological statements, one can only state that he ought to free himself from his anthropomorphic bias. The latter view, however, is of considerable significance for the philosophy of science, for it raises in a special form the general question of the unity of the pattern of scientific inquiry. I shall consider the thesis in the form presented by Nagel.

Using the statement "The function of chlorophyll in plants is to enable plants to perform photosynthesis" as a test case, Nagel offers the following as an alternative nonteleological formulation that suffers no loss of asserted content: "A necessary condition for the occurrence of photosynthesis in plants is the presence of chlorophyll." In general,

the content of the teleological statement is fully conveyed by another statement which simply asserts a necessary (or possibly a necessary and sufficient) condition for a certain trait or activity of that organism. On this assumption, therefore, a teleological explanation states the *consequences* for a given biological system of one of the latter's constituent parts or processes; the equivalent non-teleological explanation states some of the *conditions* . . . under which the system persists in its characteristic organization and activities. . . . In brief, the difference is one of selective attention, rather than of asserted content.[16]

I would make two comments on this position. The proposed translation (call it T_2) of the analysis (T_1) is not identical with T_1 in asserted content, although T_2 does not say less than T_1. On the contrary, T_2 says much more than T_1. For even if it is true that

---

[16] *Ibid.*, p. 541.

chlorophyll is necessary for photosynthesis, T_1 does not state that it is true. This can be seen if we consider that the discovery of a plant that performs photosynthesis without chlorophyll would leave T_1 true, but would falsify T_2. Nagel points out that any evidence supporting T_1 also supports T_2,[17] but this is true because T_1 is essentially weaker than T_2, although supported by the same kind of evidence. T_1 presupposes a causal relation between chlorophyll and photosynthesis, but this relation is not one of necessary condition to consequent. In this particular example one is strongly tempted to import into the translation empirical knowledge not found in the assertion. In many functional analyses, especially the more speculative ones, this temptation is absent. Consider this analysis taken from C. D. Darlington: "Facultative parthenogenesis in *Rubus* and *Rosa* and probably elsewhere also has the use that it is stimulated when pollination with another species has taken place: it thus becomes an agent of genetic isolation." [18] No geneticist would maintain that this mechanism is necessary for genetic isolation, even in the species where it is found; they would maintain at best that it does in fact prevent hybridization or the formation of inviable zygotes on some occasions.

Secondly, T_2 has the logical form of a law statement. On the usual interpretation T_2 could be true if there were no plants, or if no plants performed photosynthesis. But T_1 would surely be false if either of these conditions obtained. I do not see a way to prove this, but it seems to be clearly involved in the notion of a function. For what sense would it make to say, "If anything were a plant, then the function of chlorophyll, etc.," other than to repeat T_2? Functional analysis has existential import and to that extent belongs to natural history. To be sure, functional analysis is impossible without some knowledge of general statements. My definition makes explicit both these features of functional analysis.

But this does not prove that teleological language cannot be eliminated from biology; it merely proves that the schema directing the translation is a little more complicated. The general thesis that teleological language may be eliminated from biology invites a

[17] *Ibid.*, pp. 541–42.
[18] Darlington, "Taxonomic Species," in *New Systematics*, ed. Huxley, p. 149.

closer look. It is one thing to show that such language is in principle eliminable, and quite another to recommend the elimination. The former task may be undertaken, as it is by Nagel and others, to show that no unique principles of explanation are required in dealing with organisms. This task is clearly independent of the more sweeping recommendation. As a matter of fact, Nagel does not make that recommendation.

There are two senses in which a teleological statement may be said to be eliminable from the language of biology. (1) The elimination might be carried out by pencil-and-paper operations, in which appeal is made only to a translation schema, such as the one suggested by Nagel. For this one needs only knowledge of syntax and semantics. Or (2), the elimination may require in addition to the translation schema some empirical knowledge not explicitly asserted in the teleological statement. It is by no means plain that teleological statements which contain functional concepts are all eliminable in the first sense, even though they are eliminable in the second. If some are eliminable only in the second sense, it should be recognized that a program of elimination is nothing less than a program of further research directed toward the discovery of nonfunctional properties sufficient for the unambiguous description of, e.g., all escape reactions, danger signals, etc. And if a functional concept is polytypic with respect to the set of nonfunctional properties, elimination of that concept can only be achieved by its replacement with a *set* of concepts, which entails some loss of economy.

CHAPTER VII

Teleological Systems, Behavior, and Explanation

In this chapter an analysis of the nature of teleological systems and behavior will be presented and applied to the problem of the logic of teleological explanation. I shall examine a contemporary view of teleology—that of George Sommerhoff—and indicate the difficulties that appear in it. In attempting to overcome the difficulties, I have found it necessary to distinguish purposive behavior from the action of a system *qua* teleological. This requires some special attention to the concept of purposive behavior in order to discover its relation to teleological systems. The results yield a theory of teleological explanation and shed light on the relation of such explanation to functional analysis.

A CONTEMPORARY ACCOUNT OF TELEOLOGY

In the analysis that follows, I shall assume the general point of view toward teleology taken by R. B. Braithwaite,[1] George Sommerhoff,[2] and Ernest Nagel.[3] In their writings on this topic, they assume, and prove, that teleological language is not nonsense, and not necessarily anthropomorphic; that teleological statements do not presuppose a metaphysical doctrine of final causes; and that it has legitimate scientific uses. On the contrary, they agree unanimously that no nonphysical agents or causes need be active in teleological behavior and that no unique method of treatment is required in its explanation. In fact, the teleological system is simply

[1] Braithwaite, *Scientific Explanation*, pp. 319–41; and Braithwaite, "Teleological Explanations," in *Proceedings* N.S., Vol. XLVII.

[2] Sommerhoff, *Analytical Biology*.

[3] Nagel, "Teleological Explanation," in *Philosophy of Science*, ed. Feigl and Brodbeck; and Nagel, "Mechanistic Explanation," *Philosophy and Phenomenological Research*, XI, 330.

a special case of a physical system in the ordinary sense of that term, and can be described, *qua* teleological, in a vocabulary suited for the description of nonteleological systems. Accordingly, the methodological problem of teleology is to be regarded as a specialized problem soluble with the aid of the philosophical categories that are applied to the natural sciences in general. This study is in agreement with all these points. The problem, then, is to implement in detail the program of interpreting the concepts of "teleological system," "purposive behavior," etc., and of presenting a positive account of the logic of teleological explanation. In these details, all writers differ considerably, especially in regard to the treatment of explanation. Sommerhoff does not present an explicit analysis, but shows that phenomena that others regard as subject to teleological explanation are instances of "directively correlated behavior" and therefore describable in neutral terms.[4] Teleological analyses, I have maintained, ought to be denied the title of "explanation." Nagel is concerned with teleological analyses, and therefore his explication does not apply to the problem of strict teleological explanation.

It is customary to define "teleological system" and "teleological behavior (process, activity)" at one stroke. Since there are no fixed usages in the matter, the philosopher is entitled to considerable freedom of stipulation. C. A. Mace certainly exercises it when he defines a teleological system as one "constructed by a teleological process." [5] This diverges completely from the common model of a teleological system, which is something like an organism or self-guided missile and nothing like a statue or handkerchief. It is usual to describe in behavioral terms the form of teleological behavior, and to define a teleological system as one capable of behavior of this form. In practice, the form is described by Braithwaite, Sommerhoff, and Nagel by reference to general features of the causal relations holding within the system.[6] I have found no convenient way

---

[4] Sommerhoff, *Analytical Biology*, pp. 14, 54–55.

[5] Mace, "Mechanical and Teleological Causation," in *Philosophical Analysis*, ed. Feigl and Sellars, p. 535.

[6] Braithwaite, *Scientific Explanation*, p. 330; Sommerhoff, *Analytical Biology*, pp. 55–56; Nagel, "Teleological Explanation," in *Philosophy of Science*, ed. Feigl and Brodbeck, pp. 546–50.

to define "teleological behavior" as the behavior of a system *qua* teleological in a way that does full justice to both concepts. Accordingly, my description of a teleological system lacks the generality of the descriptions referred to, but avoids a number of difficulties.

The analysis of the concept "teleological system" does not, of course, begin in a vacuum. Everyone has at least a rough idea of the kind of behavior shown by such systems, and the task of analysis is to make this idea explicit in a way that draws a distinction of some philosophical or scientific interest. To a large extent, the outcome of the analysis depends upon the preanalytic content of the idea of a teleological system. Virtually all philosophers nowadays take as a paradigm a system in a particular state, or tending toward it, such that fortuitous variations outside the state, or deviations from the path to it, are compensated by suitable changes in the system itself. Sommerhoff and Nagel formulate this condition exactly, and introduce restrictions necessary to rule out unwanted cases, such as rivers flowing toward the sea and pendulums coming to rest. It seems to me that there are two more components in our vague idea of a teleological system. At any rate, they are considerations that have influenced my analysis, so I shall list them. First, in a teleological system, its behavior *qua* teleological involves the expenditure of energy derived from a local source rather than from the environment. The teleological system is guided, not goaded by the environment. The difficulty with the phrase "forced-movement," as a synonym for "tropism," lies in the fact that it suggests that the energy utilized in animal behavior is imparted to it by the stimulus.

Second, teleological systems involve specialized structure, a "hookup" on which the teleological behavior depends, but which could be disrupted without completely changing the nature of the system. This is perhaps the vaguest condition of the three. In the analysis, I shall attempt to clarify each of them.

These conditions are logically distinct, but in all probability they are not empirically distinct. In particular, it seems to me that any system which realizes the first two conditions will also embody the third, but this is an empirical question, and I see no proof one way or the other.

The analysis to be presented represents an attempt to avoid a number of difficulties of detail in the formulation due to Sommerhoff. He offers an analysis of certain biological terms, such as 'adaptation,' 'integration,' 'coordination,' and 'purpose-like behavior,' in what he calls 'physico-mathematical' terms.[7] Only his category of "purpose-like behavior" will be of interest to us here; however, he analyzes all the above concepts as special cases under his central concept of "directive correlation."

Any event or state of affairs Rt_1 occurring at a time t_1 is *directively correlated* to a given simultaneous event or state of affairs Et_1, in respect of the subsequent occurrence of an event or state of affairs Gt_2 [elsewhere called the "focal condition" FCt_2] if the physical system of which these are parts is objectively so conditioned that there exists an event or state of affairs CVt_0 [the coenetic variable] prior to t_1, and a set of possible alternative values of CVt_0 such that

(*a*) under the given circumstances any variation of CVt_0 within this set implies variation of both Rt_1 and Et_1;

(*b*) any such pair of varied values of Rt_1, Et_1 (as well as the pair of their actual values) is a pair of corresponding members of two correlated sets of possible values $R't_1$, $R''t_1$, $R'''t_1$, . . . and $E't_1$, $E''t_1$, $E'''t_1$, . . . , which are such that under the circumstances all pairs of corresponding members, but no other pairs, cause the subsequent occurrence of Gt_2 [FCt_2].[8]

Purpose-like behavior is now defined as directively correlated behavior in which each Et_1 is a subsequent value of CVt_0.[9] One restriction on the nature of the variables that may be said to be directively correlated is laid down: they must be "epistemically independent," i.e., any possible initial value of one must be compatible with any possible initial value of the other.[10]

Directive correlation may be illustrated as follows. Let s be a circuit with a power supply, a variable resistor, and an inductance

[7] Sommerhoff, *Analytical Biology,* pp. 25–26.

[8] *Ibid.,* pp. 55–56. This definition is subsequently generalized, but no new considerations are introduced.

[9] *Ibid.,* p. 62.

[10] *Ibid.,* p. 86. Nagel introduces the same restriction. "Teleological Explanation," in *Philosophy of Science,* ed. Feigl and Brodbeck, p. 547.

coil connected in series. There is an armature whose position is uniquely determined by the potential across the coil, and which is coupled mechanically to the variable resistor. Let the resistor and coupling be so arranged that increases (or decreases) in coil potential C cause corresponding increases (or decreases) in the value of the variable resistance, resulting in an increment (or decrement) of potential across the resistor which just compensates the original change in C. In other words, the circuit is a current or voltage regulator. It shows a number of directively correlated activities, according to the variables which we select for analysis. Let I be the circuit current, and let V be the potential across the resistor. Then Rt_1 (the value of V at t_1) is directively correlated with Et_1 (the value of C at t_1) in respect of the focal condition FCt_2 (a value of $I = k \pm d$, where k is a constant), since, in the operating system s, the values of both Et_1 and Rt_1 are jointly determined by CVt_0 (the value of C at t_0). The condition of epistemic independence is met, since any possible value of C is compatible with any possible value of V.

A different selection of variables would yield other examples of directive correlation, e.g., C is self-regulatory in the same sense as I in this circuit, and indeed its normal value can be taken as the focal condition of a pair of directively correlated variables, such as the values of resistance and the power supply voltage. In general, if the normal value of a variable is a focal condition, every variable which it uniquely determines will also be the focal condition of directively correlated pairs.

This analysis makes explicit the first prima facie condition of a teleological system which I mentioned. In addition, my example embodies the remaining two, the presence of a local energy source and a specialized hookup, namely, the mechanical coupling.

I think Sommerhoff's analysis is essentially correct, but suffers a number of difficulties in detail.

1. It is difficult to see how Sommerhoff would deal with cases of behavior which fail to achieve their focal condition but which we should nonetheless call purposive. He does state that directive correlation is present when the joint occurrence of any one of the directively correlated pairs Et_1 and Rt_1 results in a high proba-

bility of the achievement of the focal condition.[11] But even so, this condition is not weak enough. Sommerhoff is trying to take account of the following kind of situation: even the best, e.g., target-tracking mechanism, cannot guarantee hits on an elusive target; the best it could do is insure the greatest probability of hits, always leaving out of account certain factors, such as shifts in the wind, changes of the target's direction, etc., which either are not compensated by the tracking mechanism or which take place after the shot is fired but before the missile reaches its target. But there is another class of cases that this weaker formulation does not handle: all those cases in which failure to achieve the focal condition is the result of below-par functioning of the system, e.g., the clumsy attempts of a poor marksman—not a tracking mechanism—to track and hit a flying bird. Sommerhoff's picture of purposive action is a picture of success.[12] This raises the technical problem of finding a weaker formulation that admits unsuccessful activities, but which does not admit unwanted cases like the river or the pendulum.

2. The requirement that any Et_1 (or any Rt_1) must be so correlated with the corresponding Rt_1 (or Et_1) that no other pairs of values will result in the attainment of the focal condition is altogether too strong. In many cases the goal or focal condition of an activity may be so specified that for a given environmental condition Et_1 any number of responses Rt_1 may be caused by any of a set of environmental conditions Et_0 and still result in the occurrence of the focal condition. For example, if my goal is reaching a particular place, the same stimuli from that place may be directively correlated (in a weaker sense) with any of a number of responses that will result in attaining that place, and the same response may be directively correlated with a number of different stimuli from that place. Sommerhoff's idea of purpose-like behavior is hitting the bull's-eye, when it ought to be more like hitting the target.

3. In spite of the restriction of epistemic independence placed on the E and R variables, Sommerhoff fails to exclude certain degenerate cases of behavior that are evidently not purpose-like. In

[11] Sommerhoff, *Analytical Biology*, p. 110.
[12] This point was suggested to me by Professor Albert Hofstadter.

order to construct such a counterinstance, I shall first introduce some definitions. If we regard any variable as a function f of an argument x, a relation of dependence holding between an f and a class of functions $A = (g_1, g_2, \ldots, g_n)$ may be defined as follows: f is "equidependent" upon A whenever f is a single-valued function of the g's in A. If f is equidependent upon A, let the class whose members are f and the g's in A be called an L-class. The function may be either a law of nature or a mathematical theorem.

As I understand Sommerhoff, two variables are epistemically independent if and only if they do not together constitute an L-class. It is not required that they are not members of an L-class, but only that if they are, the L-class will have at least one more member. This is the sense in which E and R may be dependent, while retaining epistemic independence. Evidently, any stronger relation of independence would introduce the risk of making directive correlation impossible.

No restriction is placed upon the relations of dependence holding between the focal condition and E and R; E and R are merely said to be causes of the focal condition.

Now if we are given carte blanche power in the specification of focal conditions in a system, a class of degenerate cases of directive correlation may be introduced. Suppose that a system exemplifies a law of the form $k = F(x, y, z)$, that x and y are epistemically independent, and that a variation in x is followed by a variation in y. All these conditions may be realized if z remains constant. Then x and y are directively correlated in respect of the subsequent occurrence of the focal condition defined as the maintenance of the constant value of the function F. Notice that x and y are epistemically independent if z can vary, i.e., if this is nomically possible, and that x and y are directively correlated if Z does not in fact vary. A single resistor carrying a current represents such a system with respect to its exemplification of Ohm's law.

Such cases could no doubt be rejected within Sommerhoff's analysis by suitable *post hoc* restrictions aimed at excluding artificially constructed focal conditions. But one would have to be on guard against tossing out too much. In particular, one could not rule that E, R, and FC may not constitute an L-class; nor can the relation of independence between E and R be further loosened, e.g., by stating that they actually show independent values while the system exhibits directively correlated activity. Both proposals would exclude many systems which are prima facie teleological.

CHARACTERISTICS OF A TELEOLOGICAL SYSTEM

"Teleological system" will be defined as follows. Let s be a system, and let S be the class of state-variables $f_1, f_2, \ldots, f_n$ which define it. The environment of s is the class of all systems s' characterized by any of a class E of variables which is in turn the set-sum of every set A_i upon which any f_i in S is equidependent. Then s is a teleological system with respect to a variable h if and only if:

1) S is not an L-class
2) h is equidependent upon S, i.e., h and the members of S constitute an L-class
3) There is a class of variables B and an environmental variable g such that hεB and g is equidependent upon B
4) There is a class of variables C and a state-variable f such that gεC and f is equidependent upon C
5) If h is regarded as a function of time, then h is either restricted within a specified range of variation, or else h shows a regular pattern of change. Let both situations be represented by the expression $h = F(t)$
6) s is so constituted that it is nomically possible to alter s or its environment in such a way that condition 2) continues to hold but condition 5) does not

This definition may be illustrated by a slight modification of our original example. There we let V be the voltage across the resistor, and C the coil voltage. In addition, let P be the voltage of the power supply. Assume that there are no other voltage drops in the circuit. By hypothesis, $C = k \pm d$, so we shall let C be the h-variable. The state-variables are P and V, and the environmental variables include all those factors which can influence either P or V, e.g., changes in temperature, "stray" magnetic fields, etc. S is not an L-class, since they do not uniquely determine each other, but h together with S constitute an L-class, since, by Kirchhoff's law, the sum of the po-

tential differences around a closed circuit is zero. Conditions 3)
and 4) are realized by virtue of the mechanical hookup of coil and
resistor. Let g be the resistance of the resistor; then B may be
regarded as a unit class whose sole member is h (of course B could
be regarded as having more members). Then the members of C
are g and the circuit current, which uniquely determine, by Ohm's
law, the value of a state-variable, namely V. Condition 5) is realized by hypothesis, and condition 6) is realized since it is possible to
disconnect the coil from the resistor. In this case, the sum of V, C,
and P is still zero—Kirchhoff's law is not abrogated—but C will no
longer be approximately constant; it will vary with every chance
environmental influence.

The chief difference between this analysis and Sommerhoff's
lies in the fact that here all relevant relations of dependence have
been made explicit and in the fact that the concept of a focal condition has not been introduced. To be sure, the realization of the
condition $h = F(t)$ can be regarded as attainment of a focal condition but this would be a special case of the general concept,
which Sommerhoff intends to be an explication of the idea of the
goal or end of a purposive act. On my analysis, the changes in value
of the h-variable are an essential part of the activity of the system;
in fact, they "direct" the system. Evidently not all goals, especially
those not yet achieved, serve this function.

The analysis makes explicit the first and third components in the
preanalytic idea of a teleological system. Random deviation from
a standard condition is compensated by suitable changes in the
teleological system, and the notion of a "special hookup" is explicated in condition 6). In a sense, the working of s is due to its
exploitation of a fundamental law, viz., the one which renders the
state-variables and h an L-class. But the system also embodies additional features by which the activity of h is made causally relevant to the activities of the variables on which h depends, in a way
not described in the fundamental law. It was pointed out by D.
Gasking that when two variables, e.g., resistance and current, are
functionally related, we ordinarily regard the one as causing the
value of the other, and not vice versa, when we can give a recipe for
changing the latter simply by changing the former and not vice

versa.[13] In the teleological system an unusual recipe is embodied: e.g., in the example we have a built-in way of changing the value of a resistance by changing the value of a current. Notice further that the form of this causal dependence is not given by Ohm's law. Ohm's law is, of course, not "violated." We have a function of two arguments, current and resistance, in addition to the function of three arguments, these two plus voltage, given in Ohm's law. This additional function is in a peculiar epistemological position: like Ohm's law, it is deducible from more general laws and statements of the relevant boundary conditions. But it is so seldom exemplified that its interest as a principle capable of yielding explanations within a theory is severely limited. This is what I meant by stating that there is a "special hookup" in the teleological system. The notion of "special" is of course not precise in this context. If, however, we do characterize a law as a "special" one if it is exemplified only under such special conditions, a necessary condition of the teleological system may be stated as follows. The value of the h-variable is given by two distinct functions: the one states a more general law, whereas the other states a more special law. But —and this is of the essence of a teleological system—the arguments of the latter function are a proper subclass of the arguments of the former. The relations of dependence under which this may happen are given in conditions 3) and 4) above. This situation is necessary but not sufficient, since the other four conditions are also necessary. In particular, as an outcome of the functional dependence of h on a subclass of the state-variables, h must exhibit the behavior described in the formula $h = F(t)$.

We may now state more precisely the remaining member of my list of prima facie characteristics of a teleological system, namely, that the energy expended in directive behavior [14] is derived from a local source. The energy expended in the activity described by the law relating h to the state-variables is, by definition, derived from a local source. But, then, it is trivial to say that the work done in directive activity involves expenditure of local free energy, since

---

[13] Gasking, "Causation and Recipes," *Mind*, LXIV, 486–87.

[14] Subsequently, the behavior of a system *qua* teleological will be termed 'directive behavior' or 'activity.'

the behavior of h *is* the directive activity. Accordingly, the whole condition can be put as follows: the teleological system is distinguished from its environment (i.e., is defined by the choice of state-variables) in such a way that its energy supply must be local. If we are unable to find such a definition, this constitutes one reason for not regarding the system as teleological.

Sommerhoff says as little as possible about the physical makeup of the system which shows directively correlated activities. He states only that the system is "objectively so constituted that" it would behave so and so under stipulated conditions. I have tried to describe in a general way what this "objective constitution" consists in. I have followed the cyberneticists in holding that such systems are "feedback mechanisms." In fact, the above description of a teleological system may be regarded as an explication of the general concept of feedback, of which "positive" and "negative" feedback are both special cases.

PURPOSIVE BEHAVIOR

In order to see how this analysis avoids the difficulties in Sommerhoff's account, we must first find a more adequate account of the nature of purposive or goal-directed behavior. It will be admitted that goal-directed behavior is not identical with directive activity as I have defined it, but includes the latter and much else besides. Most people would regard, e.g., the wink-reflex as purposive, even if there is nothing like directive correlation involved in its mechanism. But more importantly, we have purposive behavior "aimed" at the attainment of some future end. Descriptions of what is involved in this idea have usually taken the form of specifications of empirically ascertainable properties of certain kinds of behavior antecedently known to be purposive, especially human behavior directed toward a conscious end-in-view. The hope has been that the properties exhibited by this behavior will also be exhibited by that behavior of other animals which we find ourselves irresistibly inclined to regard as purposive. In this way we might solve what R. B. Braithwaite considers the chief analytic problem at issue here: how to define "goal-directed" behavior that either may or may not be "goal-intended."[15] R. B. Perry offered an analysis which he believed to be acceptable for a behavioristic psychology. It consists in the presentation of a set of criteria describing the form of purposive behavior, and makes no reference whatever to the internal structure of the system engaged in it.[16] A number of modifications of Perry's list have since been offered, both by philosophers and by scientists, e.g., McDougall, Tolman, E. S. Russell, Braithwaite, and A. Hofstadter. I shall refer to all those lists of criteria which more or less approximate Perry's as the "behavioristic analysis" of teleological behavior.

This experimental concern is well exemplified in Braithwaite's definition of purposive behavior: "persistence toward the goal under varying conditions."[17] We may expand this formulation as follows, in which case we have the position stated by Perry[18] and Hofstadter:[19] an action is purposive if and only if:

1) There is a goal
2) The system shows persistence in reaching that goal; and
3) The system shows sensitivity to the conditions which support and/or impede the reaching of the goal

This behavioristic analysis has been called, for evident reasons, the "lens model" of purposive behavior.

The reader might object that the behavioristic analysis is faulty because it involves a logical circle; we are trying to define goal-directed behavior, yet the *definiens* begins with the statement "There is a goal." If we knew what a goal was, we should know what goal-directedness is. However, this difficulty can be overcome in practice—and these are intended as practical criteria—by the method of successive approximations. The goal, the persistence, and the sensitivity to conditions are, so to speak, discovered together in any particular case. If, e.g., we find an animal's behavior with the look of persistence about it, we can tentatively locate a goal, and then confirm our location by the presence of persistence and sensi-

---

[15] Braithwaite, "Teleological Explanations," in *Proceedings*, N.S., XLVII, iii.
[16] Perry, "Purpose," *Journal of Philosophy*, XVIII, 85–105.
[17] Braithwaite, "Teleological Explanations," in *Proceedings*, N.S., XLVII, viii.
[18] Perry, "Purpose," *Journal of Philosophy*, XVIII, 96.
[19] Hofstadter, "Objective Teleology," *Journal of Philosophy*, XXXVIII, 29–39.

tivity to supporting and/or impeding conditions with respect to the hypothetical goal. In any particular application of one of the three parts of our *definiens*, some knowledge of the other two is presupposed. By using the criteria, we may get successively closer to a correct identification of the goal and the precise operations of the organism we loosely call "sensitivity to conditions."

When we consider teleological explanation, we shall have to examine in greater detail the relation of the behavioristic analysis of teleological behavior to the present analysis of teleological systems. For the present, however, it is sufficient to relate them in the following manner. Suppose that a system exhibits the kind of activity described in the behavioristic analysis; this means it is possible to identify a goal. Then, I maintain, (1) the system is teleological with respect to at least one h-variable; and (2) the probability of the system's achieving the goal is greater when the h-variable shows directive activity than this probability would be if the h-variable failed to show directive activity.

It should be clearly recognized that we have here an empirical relation between purposive behavior and teleological systems, and not a logical relation between the concepts "purposive behavior" and "teleological system." The distinction between purposive behavior and directive activity does not occur in the formulation of Sommerhoff and in this sense his analysis is more general. On the other hand, the distinction allows us to circumvent the three difficulties in Sommerhoff's analysis.

1. Failure to achieve the goal, or failure to act in such a way that, under the circumstances, the greatest probability of goal-achievement is insured, does not mean that the action is not purposive. Under the present view, an action can miss its goal or can be so directed that the probability of goal-achievement is in fact much smaller than it could be; it is only necessary that the action answer to the behaviorist analysis and that the probability of goal-achievement would be still smaller if an h-variable failed to show directive activity.

2. A one-one correlation between environmental changes and possible "compensatory" reactions of the system is not a necessary feature of purposive behavior, nor, indeed, of directive activity. The

function $h = F(t)$ may be compatible with any of a wide range of combinations of values of the state-variables, and there may be a number of purposive actions which are compatible with the constancy of h, or with the normal pattern of change in the value of h.

3. The third difficulty—the existence of degenerate cases of directive correlation—is avoided in this analysis, not by means of the distinction between purposive behavior and directive activity, but by further specifications of the dependence relations holding in the teleological system. The state-variables are not merely epistemically independent; at least one of them is dependent upon the h-variable, but would not be dependent if the system or its environment were altered in a nomologically possible way.

FUNCTIONAL ANALYSIS AND
TELEOLOGICAL EXPLANATION

We must now apply these considerations to the question of the logical pattern of teleological explanation. It has been customary in recent times to explicate the difference between causal and teleological explanations in terms of a prior analysis of the distinguishing characteristics of teleological systems. The historical reason for this is plain: philosophers have been at pains to show that even in those regions of science where teleological explanations may be appropriate, the scientist is after all not concerned with subject matters which are separated from physicochemical systems by an insurmountable ontological gulf. Any possible metaphysical ground for assuming a unique nonphysical factor at work in the teleological system is cut away if it is shown that teleological systems are merely special cases of physical systems, showing their peculiar behavior in virtue of their special type of organization. I am in complete agreement with this thesis. However, it should be recognized that the step from a theory of teleological systems to a theory of teleological explanation is by no means self-evident. Indeed, I think that much of the dissatisfaction that both biologists and philosophers experience when they consider each other's views arises from the fact that this step is so often a misstep.

The largest source of trouble is failure to distinguish two very different patterns of 'teleological statements.' In order to explicate this concept, we must attend to two distinct *explicanda, viz.,* those which have been distinguished under the head of functional analyses and teleological explanations proper. I have described the pattern of functional analysis and sketched some of the relations of functional analyses to the theories in which they figure and to functional concepts. Some notable omissions, especially an explicit consideration of the type of system which may be profitably subjected to functional analysis, will now be rectified.

Functional analyses do not exhaust the class of teleological statements, however. One reason why teleological explanations have been neglected by philosophers in favor of functional analyses is the fact that such explanations have a complex pattern which conceals their peculiar teleological character. Moreover, in the literature they are usually found in extremely elliptical form, with some necessary statements left unsaid, and in this form they bear a misleadingly strong resemblance to functional analyses. Nevertheless, it will be admitted that it is possible to give an explanation, and even a strict "sufficiency" explanation, of, e.g., the sinuous path of a target-tracking torpedo in terms of the sinuous path of its target. Prima facie, this explanation would have very little in common with the bare statement "The heart beats in order to circulate the blood." Explanations of things like the path of the missile are what I call teleological explanations.

Correlative with the failure to draw this distinction is the failure of philosophers to take into account a distinction that is part of the everyday furniture of the biologist, *viz.,* the distinction between a biological end and the goal of a purposive activity.[20] Functional analyses are concerned with the former, teleological explanations with the latter. Thus, e.g., Daphnia, a crustacean, moves toward the light whenever the acidity of its habitat goes above a certain level. The biological end of this action is, no doubt, to increase the amount of available oxygen, since, in the normal habitat, the surface and the region of greatest illumination correspond; the goal is simply to reach the more illuminated region. Everyone would grant the dis-

---

[20] The distinction is drawn in various terminologies, e.g., between goal-directed and end-serving activities (Russell, *Directiveness,* p. 80), or between hormic goals and biological consequences (Agar, *Living Organism,* pp. 27–30).

tinction; the question is whether it is relevant to the analysis of teleological explanation. Prima facie, the distinction seems to be one between a narrower function and a more inclusive one: we have two activities, approaching light (F_1) and approaching oxygen (F_2), and indeed the still more inclusive functions of self-maintenance and preservation of the species. Might we not then say that the teleological explanation of the situation consists in nothing more than stating that, and in what way, the activity contributes to F_1, F_2, or perhaps to the more inclusive functions? If the difference is construed in this way, we are inclined to overlook the fact that reference to the goal, but not to any of the other functions which the action may subserve, can aid in the construction of an explanation of an entirely different pattern. Any activity that subserves one biological end, in other words, also subserves an indefinitely large number of other ends, but the goal of an activity is a special case. It is discovered not by an analysis of the adaptive significance of an activity, but by application of the criteria of purposive behavior, namely, persistence and plasticity, to the action. A goal in the sense of the behaviorist analysis is logically independent of the concept of adaptation, although, to be sure—and this is a source of confusion—purposive actions often are also adaptive, and vice versa.[21]

I have oversimplified a number of points, but this cannot be remedied until we consider explicitly the logical pattern of teleological explanations.

EXPLANATION OF DIRECTIVE ACTIVITY

It is often said that the goal of a purposive action "determines" the action. Presumably, then, the role of teleological explanation is

[21] The important concept of adaptation has perhaps been neglected in this study. A whole battery of technical terminology has grown up in the course of its analysis, e.g., the distinction between "adapted" and "adaptive," between "environmental" and "domestic" adaptation. The literature contains completely incompatible definitions of "adapted," which I shall not examine in detail, e.g., "ability to live in its environment" (Woodger, *Biological Principles,* pp. 436–37) and in "a state of equilibrium" (Ashby, "Nervous System," *Mind,* LVI, 46). Both are too narrow: the nuptial flight of the queen bee is adaptive, but it has nothing to do with the queen's ability to live or with her physiological equilibria. I think a general and satisfactory definition can be given as follows: a part, activity, etc., is adapted whenever it "contributes" (in the technical sense defined in Chapter II) to the function of self-maintenance of the species.

to exhibit the details of such determination in particular cases. The crucial question here concerns the relation of knowledge of the goal to the content of the explanation. This question must be distinguished from that of the relation of the goal itself to the behavior which is being explained. I think that failure to draw this distinction is a source of much of the lack of mutual understanding between defenders of teleology from the side of biological theory and its critics from the side of general methodology. For the biologist feels that his concern with teleology is not shown to be illegitimate by the philosophical criticisms of the doctrine of final causes; and on the other hand, the philosopher is likely to feel that the biologist has not adequately shown that his concern with teleology does not essentially involve the theory that goals are agents of their own realization. But if we apply the distinction between the relation of the goal to the activity which always or frequently achieves it, and our knowledge of the goal and the content of an *explanans* for goal-directed behavior, the prima facie conflict between biologists such as Agar and Russell and philosophers such as Reichenbach and Schlick may be resolved. The philosopher is saying that future goals do not exert effects upon the present activities which happen to achieve those goals, i.e., he is denying that a particular relation holds between goals and purpose-like actions. But the biologist is holding that we often need knowledge of a goal in order to provide content for explanation of the behavior that always or frequently achieves it. He is not contradicting the philosopher, but is maintaining a logically independent position.

The misunderstanding is exacerbated by the fact that both critics and defenders of teleology state their views in an ambiguous terminology. I refer in particular to the equivocal word 'determine.' Philosophers state that the goal does not determine the present action; the biologist may occasionally maintain that it does. Evidently, if they are not contradicting one another, 'determine' is being used in different senses. To say that X determines Y, e.g., that wind direction determines the direction in which a twig is bent, is to say, in one sense of 'determine,' that X is the efficient cause, or part of the efficient cause, of Y. This relation between X and Y is often called 'causal determination.' In another sense of the term, "X determines

Y" means that if X is given, Y is also given, or can be inferred with or without the help of synthetic principles. For example, we say that two points determine exactly one straight line; that the values of the argument-variables determine the value of the function; and that the direction of the twig's bending determines the direction of the wind. If the term is being used in this sense, we can under some conditions state truly that the future determines a past occurrence.[22]

The denial of the doctrine of final causes involves the denial that a goal causally determines the actions that may realize it, but does not deny (or affirm) that the goal may determine prior activities in the second, epistemological, sense of 'determine.' This distinction suggests that we might interpret the position of the defenders of teleology as involving no more than the assertion that the goal of purposive activity determines, in the epistemological sense, the purposive activity itself. Under such an interpretation, teleology is stripped of its suspicious trappings.

Unfortunately, the situation is much more complex, for no biologist would hold that the goal epistemologically determines the activities that realize it. On the contrary X epistemologically determines Y whenever X is a necessary condition of Y, but it is characteristic of purposive behavior that the goal Y may be achieved under a set of conditions, i.e., no particular X is necessary for Y, so Y does not epistemologically determine X.

Nevertheless, the relation that does hold between the goal and purposive activity is very closely allied to the concept of epistemological determination. I shall maintain that the goal "determines" the prior activity in the sense that knowledge of the goal is a necessary precondition of Humean explanation of the goal-seeking activity. Teleological explanation, accordingly, is a special case of ordinary "sufficiency" explanations (or quasi-explanations) in the Humean Pattern. In this special case the goal is not its own cause, but reference to the goal is a necessary condition for the construction of formally adequate explanations of the activity directed toward the goal. This is an epistemological sense of the word 'determine,' and, moreover, one which is currently accepted, for we do say that the initial and boundary conditions mentioned in Humean explanation

[22] Braithwaite, *Scientific Explanation*, pp. 336–37.

determine, or partially determine, the *explanandum*. Evidently, no mystical or other unwanted metaphysical features are implicated in this sense of teleological determination.

We must now state exactly what is meant by saying that in teleological explanation knowledge of the goal is a necessary precondition of Humean explanation of the goal-seeking activity. I define "teleological explanation" as any explanation which meets the formal requirements of the Humean Pattern, and which, in addition, satisfies the following conditions:

1) The *explanans* is directive or purposive activity, or else a property of a system that it exhibits in virtue of directive or purposive activity

2) The explanation is, or essentially involves, explanation of the behavior of an h-variable of a teleological system

3) The h-variable is effectively defined by reference to properties of the goal, or the normal activity of the h-variable is specified in terms of properties of the goal. (In the special case of explanations of directive activity, the normal activity of the h-variable, $h = F(t)$, may be the goal.)

4) The explanation is a model-explanation in virtue of one or more subsidiary hypotheses invoked for the sake of explaining the behavior of the h-variable

Philosophers have often remarked that teleological explanations are virtually worthless precisely because they are cheap. If indeed teleological explanations are as complicated as these four conditions suggest, that difficulty is by-passed, since explanations of this type would presuppose a rather high level of scientific sophistication.

We shall now consider two cases of teleological explanation: first, the explanation of a case of directive activity, and second, a case of goal-directed activity in which the goal is not identical with the directive activity of an h-variable.

Consider the following simple psychological experiment: A human subject is blindfolded and placed on a rotating stool in a soundproof room. The experimenter moves about the room, continuously sounding a buzzer. The subject is instructed to face in the direction of the buzzer. Suppose that he always succeeds, within a margin of error of d degrees. The problem is to explain how the subject manages to succeed.

I think it will be agreed that there is no question of deducing the *explanandum* from any body of data which includes essential reference to the structure of the subject's nervous system. This behavior is what the organismic biologist calls "organized." We need an explanation employing concepts appropriate to a level or organization higher than the neural level; we need a plausible model. In short, we need a teleological explanation. Let us first show that the situation involves a teleological system.

Let h be the angle between the direction in which the subject faces and the line drawn from the buzzer to the subject's forehead. Then the normal activity of the h-variable consists in maintenance of a value of $h = 0 \pm d$. We define a set of state-variables S; f_1 is the amplitude of sound at one ear; f_2 that at the other ear; and f_3 the direction the subject faces. These together do not constitute an L-class. If, for example, we know the amplitude at one ear and the direction in which the subject faces, we cannot, on this basis alone, infer the amplitude at the other ear; similarly, if we know f_1 and f_2, we cannot infer f_3. But if we add h to $S = (f_1, f_2, f_3)$, we do obtain an L-class, on the assumption that the buzzer is the only source of sound. The value of h is uniquely determined by the values of the variables in S. If we let g, an environmental variable, be the direction of the buzzer, there is a class B of variables, of which h is a member, and upon which g is equidependent: $B = (h, f_3)$. The relation of g to h and f_3 is of course not empirical, but analytic. And there is a class of variables C of which g is a member and upon which an f, say f_1, is equidependent: $C = (g, f_2, f_3)$. If we now grant, what is no doubt true, that, e.g., a brain injury could impair the subject's power to succeed in his task, the system defined by S is a teleological system, and the behavior of h constitutes directive activity.

Now consider the explanation of the formula $h = 0 \pm d$. No special assumptions need to be made about the form of the functional dependence of h upon S, other than the fully attested fact that if $h = 0$, $f_1 = f_2$, and that if $h \neq 0$, $f_1 \neq f_2$. We do, however, need to make an assumption about the function describing the members of the L-class C, namely, that if a change in g is correlated with a change in f_1, f_3 changes in such a way that f_1 and f_2 are made approximately equal. This is the critical subsidiary hypothesis that the explanatory power of the model depends upon. All four conditions of teleological explanation are satisfied: we have a model-explanation of the directive activity of a teleological system. It may be worth while to point out that here, as in teleological systems in general, h is a function of two distinct classes of argument-variables, one of which is a proper subclass of the other. The "fundamental" law gives h as a function of the state-variables; the "special" law gives h as a function of f_3 and either f_1 or f_2. The fundamental law does not depend upon any neural or other special hookup; it is derivable from the laws of physics and geometry. The special law depends for its exemplification upon the constitution of the human nervous system, in particular, a mechanism that causes the subject to compensate, under special circumstances, for any development of a differential in sound amplitude at his eardrums. Of course, the subsidiary hypothesis is subject to an independent check, and is itself susceptible of model-explanation.

This analysis of the teleological explanation, since I have shown in detail that the system and explanation are both teleological in the senses defined, is considerably more complex than the explanation itself. In its elliptical form, the explanation would be approximately as follows: "The subject faces the buzzer because he moves his head in such a way that the amplitude of sound at his two eardrums is maintained at approximately equal values." The advantage of my more detailed statement lies in its exhibition of the precise nature of the subsidiary hypothesis and in its showing the peculiar role in the explanation of knowledge of the goal.

The latter point constitutes the justification for calling the explanation "teleological." The essence of teleological explanation lies in the epistemological priority of knowledge of the goal in relation to the content of the explanation. A prior knowledge of the goal of the subject's bodily movements dictated the choice of state- and environmental variables utilized in the explanation, and the explanation is of such a form that h itself, in terms of which the goal is defined, is a causal factor in the continued realization of the goal. This comes very close to saying that the goal is an agent in its own realization—the formulation so unacceptable to many philosophers. But, of course, the future is not acting upon the past, nor is the goal itself an agent. It is true, however, that in specifying the details of the feedback mechanism, deviations from the norm in terms of which the goal is defined are assumed to possess causal efficacy.

Under what circumstances are teleological explanations of directive activity useful? And when do they possess wider scientific interest? The answers to these two questions are different. Teleological explanations of the behavior of an h-variable are useful when we are interested, not in the relation of the h-variable to the state-variables on which it depends, but in the relation of the h-variable to environmental variables. This distinction may be put quite generally as follows: a variable may be viewed as a function of the arguments upon which it is equidependent, or as a function of time. In general, the mathematical form of these two functions is different, and in a teleological system, the h-variable is a function of time that possesses a relatively simple form. But it is not the flow of time itself that interests the biologist, but the fact that the directive activity of the h-variable represents a complete independence [23] of the h-variable with respect to large subclasses of the total class of environmental variables upon which h is in fact equidependent. For example, in the self-regulating circuit, current is a regular function of time, in this case a constant. The regulating property of the circuit of course depends upon the functional relations of h and the state-variables; but if, for any reason, we are interested in the regulating property, it is the independence of current with respect to those relevant environmental variables which are most likely to vary fortuitously, e.g., battery voltages, that arrests our attention and calls for explanation.

If we push the question one step further and ask why we should be especially interested in the independence of a variable h with respect to variables that do vary and which do exert causal influences on h, we may give two general answers. It may be the case that the larger system of which the teleological system is a part

[23] By "f is independent of the variables in A," I mean, in this context, that f is not equidependent upon A.

shows behavior that is for the most part directive, and that the state of knowledge of the larger system is inadequate for the formation of nonteleological explanations. Thus we must find some teleological explanations if we wish to understand some aspects of the behavior of the larger system at all. This is the case with many types of organic systems. Secondly, it may be that directive activity is a necessary condition of the persistence of the larger system, and an understanding of its persistence thus involves explanation of behavior *qua* directive.

The circumstances under which a particular teleological explanation possesses a wider scientific interest are perhaps not so evident. Of course, one might simply want to know why, e.g., a man is able to face a moving buzzer. And the explanation may provide further interesting bits of lore that might turn out to be of great use, e.g., that a man's ears are very sensitive indeed to sound differentials, and that the nervous system contains feedback mechanisms that may be switched on and off at will. But it remains true that, prima facie, we should expect a teleological explanation, in itself, to provide little material for the further theoretical advance of science. For, as we have noted, the *explanandum* is not explained by formulating a higher level and more general hypothesis, one which we could use to explain other phenomena. The subsidiary hypotheses which are introduced are likely to be exemplified only under the conditions encountered in the class of teleological systems in question, and, of course, a law cannot be invoked to describe a system in which it is not exemplified.

I think that this point is true, and that consequently the development of a biological theory, consisting of a hierarchically arranged deductive system of laws of increasing generality, is unlikely to be substantially implemented, at least directly, by the quest for teleological explanations. To this extent, the claims of some organismic biologists for the fruitfulness of teleological methods must be put down as exaggerated. I will discuss later, however, a way in which the development of such deductive theories is indirectly aided by the quest for teleological explanations.

There is, nevertheless, another side to the development of biological theory which is aided to an incalculable extent by teleological explanations, even those which are *post hoc* and nonpredictive. Teleological explanations provide, not general hypotheses, but data, of a natural historical character, data which in turn suggest and provide evidence for further hypotheses. This aspect is most evident in teleological explanations within evolution theory. For notice that the process of change or of persistence that is subject to teleological explanation may not be short and isolated, but may be long, even if measured by geological time, and may leave in its wake a multitude of collateral effects. A good teleological explanation provides both a way of filling gaps in the process for which direct evidence may be missing, and, by way of the model subsidiary hypotheses, a way of inferring some things about environmental changes which accompany the directive process. This topic will be resumed when we come to discuss evolution theory, where it will be shown that evolving populations are teleological systems, and that many explanations utilizing the principles of neo-Darwinism are teleological explanations. For the present, a hypothetical example must suffice for illustrating the principle. Suppose we have two species of insects, and that one is a mimic of the other. It would be possible to work out a measure of degree of resemblance between mimic and model, and to let the value of this measure be the h-variable of a teleological system whose state-variables are a measure of superficial characters of the model-species and a set of frequencies of genes in the mimic-species. On this basis a teleological explanation of the superficial characters of the mimic could be drawn up. The case is precisely analogous to the buzzer experiment: in both, the h-variable is identified as a relation between a state- and an environmental variable. Now any subsidiary hypothesis that can explain the regular development of the h-variable will include some reference to the selection coefficients of the relevant state-variables. This provides strong grounds for inference to the nature of the predation to which the insects are subjected. Any fossil evidence for the appearance of either mimic or model is evidence for the appearance of its opposite number. The hypothesis may in addition provide a prediction of the actual relative frequencies of mimic and model individuals in the region where they overlap, and so on.

EXPLANATIONS OF GOAL-DIRECTED BEHAVIOR

We shall now consider teleological explanations of goal-directed behavior in which the goal is not simply the directive activity of an h-variable, but a state or situation whose achievement depends upon such directive activity. It is here that the use of teleological explanation as a tool for dealing with phenomena of a high level of organization is most apparent.

As a paradigm example consider again the case of a fish which swims for cover in a hole in a reef when it is attacked by a shark. The goal—which is identified by the behaviorist criteria—is reaching the hole; the *explanadum* is the path of the fish. Suppose that under some conditions the fish swims directly for the hole; under others, when it is partially cut off by the attacker, it takes a more circuitous path. The problem is to find an explanation, a model one to be sure, which accounts for all these paths.

The details of the situation have been left deliberately vague, since greater precision would only obscure the central point. Let h in this case be the ratio of the distance between the fish and the shark to the distance between the shark and the hole. Suppose that the directive activity consists of the fish moving in such a way that h is the maximum possible under the circumstances. The state-variables S are the position of the shark (f_1), the position of the fish (f_2), and the distance between the fish and the hole (f_3). It is easy to see that S is not an L-class, but that S together with h does constitute an L-class, by virtue of the rules of geometry. Let the environmental variable g be the distance of the shark from the fish. The system consisting of fish, shark, and hole is thus a teleological system, on the assumption that, e.g., blinding the fish destroys the directive activity, since the value of h influences the value of g, and the value of g in turn influences the value of f_2. The directive activity is explained by the introduction of a subsidiary hypothesis which states that any decrease in the value of g is compensated by a change in the value of f_2 which decreases the value of f_3.

The points to notice about this explanation are the following. Attaining of the goal, achieving cover in the hole, is not itself a directive activity, but is made more probable by the occurrence of a directive activity. But, and this is the essential point, the goal and the h-variable are not defined independently of each other. The hole, an object in the environment of the fish, is explicitly mentioned in both the definition of the goal and the h-variable. There is an additional relation between the goal and the normal behavior of h in this particular case: the h-variable tends toward a maximum, and becomes infinite when the goal is achieved. Thus there is explicit reference to the goal of a directive activity in construction of model–quasi-explanation of the activity that is goal-directed.

Suppose that an ethologist wants to construct an explanation of this behavior in terms of the concepts of stimulus and response. Then even the rudimentary teleological explanation which I have outlined would be an invaluable guide. It would be necessary to describe sets of responses and sets of stimuli in such a way that general laws could be written which connect them and which yield an explanation of the fact that the fish attains the goal in a particular case. This would be an insuperable task without the use of the concept of a "cue," or an equivalent concept, i.e., one which effectively describes stimuli, not in terms of physical properties of sound, light, etc., but in terms of relations between external "macroscopic" objects. It is a fact of considerable interest in this connection that in both ethology and behavior theory the description of stimuli has largely yielded to the description of cues. A latent reference to objects and relations between them is part of the logical grammar of "cue," but not of "stimulus": we speak of cues of distance, position, orientation, etc., but not of stimuli of distance, etc. The replacement of the stimulus concept with the cue concept has accompanied the shift within behavior theory from a physiological to a molar point of view. I wish to call attention to the fact that the concept of "cue" is of greater use than the concept of "stimulus" in dealing with purposive behavior. A particular cue is effectively defined in relation to environmental objects. The cue concept is thus an instrument for dealing with behavior at the level of organization shown in purposive behavior. Both functional analysis and teleological explanation aid in the selection of the aspects of the environment relevant for the effective definition of concepts for use in the explanation of behavior. In general, we may say that teleological explanations, or even quasi-explanations, direct the formation of model subsidiary hypotheses which, even if they are not true, do contain concepts which have a good chance of proving useful in nonteleological hypotheses. This seems to me a very important indirect contribution that teleological explanations make to the theory of higher-level phenomena.

CHAPTER VIII

Selection Theory

The logic of explanation in evolution theory exhibits a number of points of interest for the philosopher of science. The purpose of the present chapter is to indicate where some of these points lie and to indicate how some of the arguments presented in previous chapters bear upon them. The scientific interest of modern evolution theory derives from its success in integrating into a single body of theory the results and data from the most diverse branches of biology: paleontology, genetics, ethology, systematics, biogeography, ecology, etc. It is of philosophical interest to see how this is accomplished, for these sciences show a staggering diversity of content and principles. If one looks at the generalizations that are enunciated by biologists, e.g., Williston's and Dollo's laws in paleontology; the ecological rules of Bergmann and Allen; the laws of segregation and independent assortment; descriptions of instinctive behavior and embryological development; and if one remembers that most of these principles have numerous exceptions, it is easy to see that the obstacles in the way of theoretical unification are very great indeed. In fact, if we look in evolution theory for the pattern of theoretical explanation exemplified in that paradigm of theory formation, Newton's explanation of Galileo's and Kepler's laws, we shall be disappointed. Evolution theory does not attain its ends by exhibiting, e.g., Williston's and Bergmann's principles as consequences of one or more hypotheses of greater generality. There are a number of small hierarchies of this character scattered about evolution theory, but the theory as a whole does not approach this type of organization. It is impossible to be dogmatic on the point, but it does seem to be true that this fact is not due to the undeveloped state of biology, but to the nature of biological subject matter. Some biologists seem to think that greater order could be brought into their science by a single genius of the caliber of a Newton. And though one cannot say that in the nature

of the case a Newton for biology will not in time appear, one can
venture to say that, in so far as the theory of evolution is concerned,
further advances in theory will not effect a revolution, but will result in filling out a sketch whose outlines are already apparent. My
own view is that evolution theory consists of a family of related
models; that most evolutionary explanations are based upon assumptions that, in the individual case, are not highly confirmed; but that
the various models in the theory provide evidential support for their
neighbors. The subsidiary hypotheses and assumptions that are made
for the sake of particular explanations in one model recur again and
again in other related models, with or without modification and
local adaptation. To use the metaphor of Agnes Arber, biological
theory is less "linear" than, e.g., physical theory, and is more "retic-
ulate." [1]

Evolution theory is of philosophical interest because of the way
it integrates principles of the most diverse sorts, but, in addition,
it is of interest because here we find the most diverse patterns of
concept formation and explanation unified in a single theory. The
technical vocabulary of evolution theory is replete with historical
and functional concepts and with concepts that are polytypic with
respect to the physical and chemical properties that have proved of
such great value in the other natural sciences. Both genetic and
functional analysis play important roles in model-building, and
many of these models yield genetic and teleological explanations.
Enough has been said, perhaps, about the relation of genetic analysis and explanation to evolution theory. I shall add, however, a
number of points about functional analysis and teleological explanation in so far as they bear upon contemporary selection theory.

THE NATURE OF SELECTION THEORY

When I speak of evolution theory, I mean that contemporary
body of theory that goes by the name of neo-Darwinism, neo-
Mendelism, the "synthetic theory," or simply "selection theory"—the
term I shall use subsequently. However one chooses to characterize
the theory, its fundamentally Darwinian cast is recognized by even
those students who retain serious reservations about the importance

[1] Arber, *The Mind and the Eye*, p. 46.

of natural selection. But evolution theory has advanced far beyond its Darwinian beginnings. This is due in large part to the application of the principles and techniques of genetics, especially population genetics, to the problems of evolution. We have, in pure form as it were, the empirical and epistemological conditions that suggest and call for the use of models. The field of evolutionary phenomena exhibits, in Rashevsky's words, a "tremendous complexity of functions." [2] Data about these phenomena have been collected for centuries and deposited in the archives by an army of professionals and amateurs—for in biology even the intelligent country gentleman or lady of leisure may make significant contributions. Such data have yielded a vast number of empirical generalizations of very restricted generality, but remarkably few that can occur as higher-level hypotheses in a scientific deductive system.

Genetics is an exception. The principles of heredity constitute a highly articulated theoretical system, one which, as Woodger has shown, is susceptible of axiomatic treatment. Moreover, the systems studied by the geneticist are physical parts of the systems that show the phenomena of interest to the student of evolution, and the workings of heredity, of course, have direct bearings on these phenomena. Accordingly, the principles of genetics may be regarded as possible candidates for the role of primary subject-descriptions in model-explanations of evolutionary phenomena. The subject-systems themselves are genes and chromosomes, and any other systems that are postulated or known to account for the behavior of chromosomes (e.g., at meiosis) or for genic action.

Selection theory is a family of related models that explain or quasi-explain empirical generalizations and particular facts of evolution. The way in which selection theory effects a unification is to be sought in the relations between the models that are applied over the whole range of questions that the fact of evolution raises, e.g., questions about the origin of species and of the taxa of higher rank, the rates of evolutionary change, the development of adaptations, etc. Among the factors which operate in achieving unification I wish to emphasize the following.

1. There is a class of principles that appear frequently in evolu-

[2] Rashevsky, *Mathematical Biophysics*, p. 355.

tionary models of the most diverse sorts. These include the primary subject descriptions of genetic systems, e.g., Mendel's laws, and the laws of population genetics, especially the Hardy-Weinberg law.

2. Specific types of subsidiary hypotheses recur. By a "type" of hypothesis in this connection is meant, e.g., the class of hypotheses about the breeding system in a population (whether random crossing, selfing, etc.); about rates of mutation or of migration; about the type of inheritance shown by a factor (whether autosomal, recessive, sex-influenced, etc.); and so on. It is important to notice that, in this somewhat vague sense of the word "type," selection theory employs fewer types of subsidiary hypotheses than there are types of generalizations to be explained. This is one justification for calling the family of models a "theory." It should also be noticed that 1) and 2) are not sharply separable, although the difference is clear enough in most particular cases. For it is sometimes possible to regard the introduction of a particular subsidiary hypothesis as the specification of a parameter that occurs in an established law.

3. There are a relatively small number of rules that direct the introduction of simplifying assumptions and subsidiary hypotheses. They specify the factors that need to be taken into account in the construction of models. In general, it is far easier to learn that one variable is a function of another than to learn what other variables are relevant or to write the form of the function. These rules of relevance, as we may term them, in large measure have been derived from models constructed for special purposes in the past. They enjoin the biologist to consider, e.g., the effects of population size, differential migration, geographical and other forms of isolation, parthenogenesis, the sex ratio, etc. To be sure, these rules are closely connected with empirical laws, and might even be said to be empirical laws. But on the whole they are not susceptible of formulation with the degree of precision requisite for usable laws.

This conception of the nature of selection theory, it appears to me, successfully interprets a number of peculiarities in the logic of evolutionary explanations that have disturbed a number of commentators. For it does have peculiarities; otherwise the completely contradictory methodological criticisms that have been aimed at evolution theory would seem completely inexplicable. It is commonly held that

Darwin provided the biologist with a "causal" theory of evolution, and that there is much in the fossil record that the theory is incapable of explaining.[3] But contemporary critics have held that there is after all little or nothing that could be properly termed a "theory" of evolution; [4] that evolution theory does not provide causal explanations; [5] and that the theory is so elastic that it can be accommodated to any empirical facts.[6] This set of counterclaims can be explained as the result of emphasis upon certain features of selection theory as a set of models.

By-passing for the moment the question of what leads a philosopher to deny the title of "theory" to neo-Darwinism, let us look at the charge that selection theory is irrefutable. The charge may take two forms. A number of phenomena have given the selectionist cause for embarrassment. In accounting for them, some writers have, by giving the appearance of grasping for straws, invited the accusation that their attitude toward selection theory is not dictated by the facts alone. The existence of long-term evolutionary trends that may have been adaptive in their early stages but which apparently continued to the point where they are positively disadvantageous has been particularly embarrassing, since such trends, prima facie, could not have been directed by natural selection. Von Bertalanffy points out with exasperation that some twenty distinct kinds of explanation for these phenomena have been offered; [7] Simpson, for example, enumerates eight possible mechanisms.[8] Are some subspecific differences nonadaptive? Selection theory is compatible with either alternative. If all are adaptive, the differences may be accounted for by the action of natural selection; if some are not adap-

---

[3] Nowadays the critics of neo-Darwinism concentrate their attention on its alleged failure to account for large discontinuities in phylogenetic lines and for the origin of higher taxa. See Goldschmidt, *Basis of Evolution,* especially pp. 6–7, 396–99.

[4] "As to the facts [of evolution], nothing or next to nothing is left to be desired. On the other hand, it seems that there is as yet hardly any theory at all. For the observation that a species best fitted to a certain environment will ultimately replace other less fortunate ones is either a pseudo-teleological truism or a tautology." Bergmann, "Psychoanalysis," in *Psychological Theory,* ed. Marx, p. 357.

[5] Woodger, *Biological Principles,* p. 399.

[6] "A lover of paradox could say that the main objection to selection theory is that it cannot be disproved." Von Bertalanffy, *Problems of Life,* p. 89.

[7] *Ibid.,* p. 88.   [8] Simpson, *Major Features,* p. 289.

tive, the differences may be due to accidents of sampling, i.e., to the much discussed Sewall Wright effect. Can selection theory account for the development of organs whose advantage to the organism is almost vanishingly minute, e.g., the fly-whisk tail of cattle? Fisher's answer is yes.[9] These examples could be multiplied; suffice it to say that the selectionist is unconvinced by any of the difficulties presented by his critics.

A related line of criticism, based upon an analysis of particular explanations rather than upon a survey of selection theory as a whole, is presented by Woodger and Gallie. They argue that selectionist explanations in point of fact simply assume everything that is needed in order to make the explanation work.[10] Thus the explanation of the giraffe's long neck assumes such things as food shortages (that somehow do not affect the young), suitable variations in neck length coupled with appropriate concomitant variations in other organs, etc., assumptions which are supported by no independent evidence. Such explanations, in so far as they pretend to the status of "sufficiency" explanations, are "question begging," "spurious," and "fallacious."

These criticisms call attention to genuine features of the logic of selection theory, but they seriously neglect a number of accompanying features that mitigate the harshness of the final verdict. Consider Von Bertalanffy's criticism. No discredit is cast upon selection theory by showing that it is in fact compatible with all available evidence. On the contrary, discredit would accrue only if it were shown to be compatible with all possible evidence. Von Bertalanffy does not attempt to maintain the stronger thesis, and, in point of fact, it could not be seriously held, since it is easy to imagine a collection of evidence which would refute the theory beyond any reasonable doubt. Moreover, he is really worried, not by the irrefutable character of selection theory, but by his conviction that it does not give a satisfactory picture of a number of facts, namely, those facts which have disturbed Schindewolf, Goldschmidt, Rensch, and other critics of selection theory.[11]

[9] Fisher, "Criticisms of Natural Selection," in *Evolution as a Process*, ed. Huxley, Hardy, and Ford, pp. 93–96.
[10] Woodger, *Biological Principles*, p. 401; and Gallie, "Explanations," *Mind*, LXIV, 169.
[11] Von Bertalanffy, *Problems of Life*, pp. 104–5.

We might say that Von Bertalanffy is really dissatisfied with the theoretical form of selection theory, and not with its success in explaining the facts. Selectionists have devoted a great deal of effort to the construction of models that are aimed at demonstrating that some observed or suspected phenomena are possible, that is, that they are compatible with the established or confirmed biological hypotheses, in particular, the hypotheses of genetics. We have already mentioned some examples, namely, the model-explanations of the origin of the chordates, the evolution of dominance, the evolution of genetic isolating mechanisms, and the occurrence of hypertelic or otherwise dysteleological trends. These models all state roughly that if conditions were (or are) so and so, then, the laws of genetics being what they are, the phenomena in question must occur. The assumptions may not be known to be true, but they are known to be not impossible. The role of models in establishing the compatibility of a phenomenon with an established theory has been discussed, but one further point is relevant here. When Simpson constructs a model of the development of an inadaptive character, by reference, e.g., to the phenomena of juvenile selection, he is not saying that a particular trend is explained by the model, but only that phenomena of this class are possible under such and such conditions. There may be other models which equally well account for the same class of phenomena, and the operation of one does not necessarily preclude the operation of others. In what sense, then, does the model explain the particular case? It at least quasi-explains it, but most importantly, it not merely demonstrates that the phenomenon is explicable in terms of well-established principles; the model itself directs any further research into the details of the historical situation that might permit elimination of the simplifying assumptions and subsidiary hypotheses. Moreover, if a model at least quasi-explains a phenomenon, the occurrence of the phenomenon lends some support to whatever subsidiary hypotheses have been introduced, but it supports only their conjunction, not each individual hypothesis. If, then, independent evidence against a particular hypothesis in a model is discovered, or if a hypothesis incompatible with it is supported by another model of the same or other phenomena, the first model provides a focus, as it were, for correcting the remaining set of subsidiary hypotheses. This is one reason for casting even those models which are known to yield only quasi-explanations in the logical form of the Humean Pattern. Delivering a final verdict of "question begging," "spurious," or "fallacious" upon particular model-explanations overlooks these all-important considerations.

I think Von Bertalanffy's criticisms stem also from an additional motive. Models in selection theory have the function, among others, of showing that the concepts which have proved to be fruitful ingredients in the laws governing one class of phenomena are capable of use in hypotheses for explaining other classes of phenomena. The organismic biologist has a constitutional dislike of such a procedure; he would prefer a new set of concepts, with laws to match, that will deal with the new phenomena in their own terms. Both of these grounds for dissatisfaction are expressed in the following passage.

From the viewpoint of science, we are not satisfied with the meagre answer that all this [—"the wealth of color, form and other creations"—] is possible within the range of the established factors of evolution. . . . We rather want to know the "secret law" at which "the chorus hints." [12]

Woodger and Gallie object to the liberties the selectionist allows himself in the introduction of subsidiary hypotheses and other assumptions. But, I have maintained, if we are to allow the advantages of model-building at all, we have to allow the necessary techniques. It should be said that neither Woodger nor Gallie denies all value to such explanations as Darwin's explanation of the development of the giraffe's neck; they merely say they are not what they purport to be, *viz.*, genuinely causal "sufficiency" explanations. I would maintain, however, that whereas they have correctly construed an element of their logical form, they have neglected the epistemological functions of these explanations.

The two objections that selection theory is not properly speaking a theory at all, and that it provides no causal explanations, are based upon the same point, namely, that although selection theory provides genetic explanations, it does not provide explanations of a predictive character.[13] It may be helpful to draw a distinction here. One

---

[12] *Ibid.*, p. 107.

[13] Woodger, as I have noted, adds the point that evolution is unique, and that causal explanations presuppose repeatability. The answer to this objection is that not every phylogenetic line is unique in every respect.

might wish to call an explanation "predictive" only if the explanation could have been constructed by a scientist, using only the theory that enters into the explanation, without knowledge that the phenomenon to be explained would in fact occur. The case of a biologist constructing an explanation of the giraffe's long neck, while confronted with the giraffe as an accomplished fact, would therefore not be a case of predictive explanation, if the biologist actually used his knowledge of the outcome of giraffe evolution in drawing up his list of assumptions. But one might wish to call an explanation predictive, even if constructed after the fact, whenever the *explanans* lays down sufficient conditions for the *explanandum*. These are respectively epistemological and logical senses of the term 'predictive.' Now it is true that most models in selection theory are not predictive in the first sense, but they are predictive in the second. And predictiveness in the second sense is all that is necessary to render an explanation "causal."

TELEOLOGICAL EXPLANATION IN
SELECTION THEORY

Explanations in selection theory not only achieve a high degree of unification of a subject matter; they also exhibit a similar unification of modes of theoretical analysis. We shall now consider the roles of teleological analysis and explanation in the theory.

There is a large class of models in selection theory which yield teleological explanations. To use one of the simplest cases to illustrate the principle, suppose that we want to explain the constancy of the frequency of a phenotype in a given population. Assume the simplest situation, in which there are three phenotypes whose defining characters are determined by the three possible pairs of alleles A_1A_1, A_1A_2, and A_2A_2. If we assume that the different pairs confer different degrees of advantage in the quest for life, or different degrees of fertility on their possessors, we may construct a model to explain, say, the constancy of frequency p_2 of the heterozygote as follows: assume that the heterozygote is the fittest, or most fertile, or both; then p_2 is determined at the beginning of one generation by the frequencies of each phenotype, p_1, p_2, and p_3 at the beginning of the last generation, together with the values of the relative selective advantages of each phenotype, a, b, and c respectively. By hypothesis, b is larger than either a or c. The existence of a feedback effect can be seen intuitively under these conditions. If, for example, the relative frequency of either class of homozygotes changes radically between breeding seasons, e.g., by an accidental decimation of the ranks of the members of the favored phenotype, the compensation will begin at breeding, in accordance with the Hardy-Weinberg law, and will continue through the differential death rates of the less favored phenotypes. Overcompensation for a chance deviation is prevented by the fact that even a wholly heterozygous population will by chance reproduce only one-half heterozygous in the succeeding generation. Chance increases in frequency of the homozygotes are compensated in the long run by selection against them; chance decreases in the frequency of either homozygote are compensated by the resultant increase in the frequency of the other homozygote, with selection against it. As many writers have noticed, this model accounts neatly for the maintenance in a population of an unfavorable gene, even one which is lethal when present in double dose. The mechanism is probably responsible for many cases of polymorphism in nature.

A population subject to such balanced selection is a teleological system. If we let p_2 be an h-variable, the factors mentioned that determine p_2 are the state-variables; the feedback is the literal feeding of alleles, in suitable proportions, into the gene pool of the population. Fisher, to whom this model is due, shows that under the assumptions the ratio of A_1 to A_2 in the population stays in the neighborhood of the ratio b-c/b-a.[14] We may accordingly conceive of either gene-frequency as the mediating environmental variable of the teleological system.

This explanation is a case of model-explanation of the normal value of an h-variable, and is therefore a teleological explanation, as I have defined this term.

Of course, this model is a special case, and may indeed apply to few phenomena in nature, although it is easy to imagine situations in which an organism that is intermediate in, e.g., size, would have the advantage over his relatives at either extreme. More often, selection moves a gene-frequency toward the limiting values of unity or

[14] Fisher, *Genetical Theory*, p. 100.

zero, or toward an equilibrium-value determined by mutation and migration rates. But this merely makes the model more complicated. We still have to explain the regular behavior of an h-variable. Simpson's conception of a self-braking trend represents another special case, although the genetic system assumed would be more complex than the pair of alleles in a Mendelian population assumed here.[15]

These explanations are teleological, but not because they employ an allegedy teleological conception such as the "survival of the fittest." The concept of natural selection never was a teleological concept, and it has in fact undergone considerable modification since the publication of *The Origin of Species*. Simpson defines natural selection as differential reproduction.[16] It is thus possible to speak of the natural selection not merely of organisms, but of genes, chromosomes, genotypes, populations—in fact, anything that reproduces. It is clear that differential reproduction is the important factor in evolution, and that consequently adaptation to the environment is relevant to evolution only in so far as it is necessary for reproduction at all. A very king among lions would leave no mark on the history of his kind if he showed a perverse preference for leopards rather than lionesses. This definition of natural selection, which incidentally includes sexual selection as a special type, has an important consequence for the logic of functional analysis. It pinpoints the stage at which the biologist may break off the chain of functional analyses, since any further analysis will yield no information usable in evolution theory itself. And any function other than self-reproduction of the species, such as organic self-maintenance, if it is chosen as the final function relevant in functional analysis, would lead the biologist to overlook many possible evolutionary models, e.g., those explaining the origin of sexless castes in insect societies.

The most important theoretical use of functional analysis in evolution theory lies in its provision of data for use in selectionist models. The estimation of measures of selective advantage are a necessary part of the application of any selectionist teleological model. Fisher's model of balanced selection, for example, cannot be applied to a particular case without a functional analysis of the

---

[15] Simpson, *Major Features*, p. 152.
[16] Simpson, *Meaning of Evolution*, p. 221.

phenotypic characters concerned. This is a simple, almost, I fear, painfully obvious fact. Yet I am sure it is overlooked by those biologists who are concerned with defending the propriety of teleological thought, since they do not mention the point in discussing the subject, in spite of its decisive bearing, as it seems to me, on their claims. If one examines an isolated functional analysis, e.g., "A cow's tail functions as a fly-whisk," it is possible to be plunged into the deepest perplexity concerning its significance. The result is too often a fruitless interchange of charges and defenses about hidden anthropomorphisms, ends-in-view, and so on.

The functional analysis does not automatically provide an explanation, but provides data for use in teleological and other model-explanations. To say that X is the function of Y is to say less than "Y is necessary for X" or "Y is sufficient for X"; but these stronger statements, although they also provide information that can be used in the construction of selectionist models, state more about Y than is required for use in most models. Consider for example the chain of functional analyses of the cow's tail: the tail contributes to keeping flies and other pests away, which in turn contributes to self-maintenance, which again contributes to self-reproduction of the species. The first two links in the chain, for example, state that there is some environment in which a tailless cow would die through the activity of pests, and in which a cow with a tail would survive; it does not state that cows actually encounter this environment frequently. In order to use the information in a model, some estimate has to be made of this frequency, on the basis, of course, of knowledge of the natural history of cows, the parasitic or disease-bearing propensities of flies, etc. One of the most important results of the models of Fisher, Haldane, and Wright consists in showing that this frequency may be of a very small order of magnitude and nevertheless be effective in evolution.

I would place the policy of seeking functional analysis in the third of our list of factors that aid in achieving unity in evolution theory, since functional analysis does direct the formation of particular subsidiary hypotheses in the application of models to individual cases. The so-called "principle of natural selection" is best understood in relation to functional analysis. As a number of writers have noticed, the principle, which can be stated in a number of alternative ways, e.g., "The more fit reproduce themselves more frequently than the less fit," bears a strong analogy to the principles of thermodynamics, especially the law of conservation of energy. It does have a prima facie resemblance to a tautology, and is indeed sometimes held to be one, since in the last resort it is possible to say that any encountered differential in rate of reproduction is due to a difference in fitness of the organism. This does not mean that the principle must be useless, however, as conventionalism has shown. Among other things, it directs the biologist to look for signs of differential reproduction and to correlate them with factors that are known to influence fitness, e.g., resistance to disease, dispersal mechanisms, etc. Secondly, the principle does not itself convey information about the direction and rate of change of an evolving system, but rather places limits upon the kind of change that can happen. Finally, it is applicable only to systems which satisfy certain very general requirements. But if these conditions are satisfied, the principle can be written in a specified form (with the help of other parts of selection theory) and initial values assigned to the parameters. In all these respects the principle parallels the law of conservation of energy.

A functional analysis of a characteristic, or of differences within a population or between populations, shows whether or not the technique of applying a selectionist model is appropriate. In this respect discovery of functional significance is like determining that a physical system may be treated as isolated. In addition, it is the first step in construction and application of a model that would yield at least quasi-explanation of the character or difference. Much biological writing, especially in ecology, may be construed as the beginning of model-construction which is not carried to completion. An ecologist may content himself with pointing out, e.g., that fish in swift streams tend to be rounded like a trout, while lake fish tend to be flattened like perch, and that this has adaptive significance, since a rounded fish is less likely to be caught up by a swift current. There would be little point in constructing a complete model to account for the evolution of these characteristics in brook and lake fish.

There is one final relation of functional analysis to natural selection that should be mentioned in this connection. We have maintained that functional analysis plays a role in the formation of higher-level concepts, i.e., concepts which are E-defined by reference to phenomena of a level of organization above the physical, chemical, or cellular level. There are many perspectives within which higher-level concepts could be formed, but the perspective which views the organism as a reproducer of its species is the perspective which gives us our description of the organism as a seeker of food and shelter and mates, a protector of the young, a user of fang and claw and wing, a system that performs metabolic functions, that coordinates its activities, and a thing of skin and limbs, kidney and liver. The organism is all these things "objectively"; of course, it is also a thing of atoms, molecules, and cells; and a system susceptible of physical analysis, etc. No doubt it is also many other interesting things which no one has thought of calling it. But when a concept C is so defined that it can appear in true functional analyses of the form "The function of C is . . . ," C is most likely to be of use in the construction of subsidiary hypotheses in selectionist models. In fact, its usefulness is enhanced if the structures, processes, etc., which constitute the extension of C are subject only to functional analysis by reference to functions near the top of the hierarchy. Such concepts need not be functional, but, as I have maintained, a functional concept may enable the construction of evolutionary models of wider scope than would otherwise be possible. In short, functional analysis directs the formation of concepts which are preeminently useful in selection theory.

CHAPTER IX

Organization and
Organismic Biology

The realization among biologists that the characteristic properties of living things are not dependent upon the presence of a special "living substance"—protoplasm—or a special ingredient, but upon ordinary chemical substances organized in extraordinary ways, brought about a great deal of speculation about the "nature" of organization. Many biologists have endowed organization with all the mysteries of life itself, and have indeed seen in organization a magical agent. Woodger collects and presents a number of passages in which biologists speak of organization as if it has "to be 'postulated,' 'recognized,' 'ascribed,' 'assumed,' etc." [1] The wide use of the term 'organizing relation' is a residue of this tendency: the term seems to imply that these relations *do* something—something inscrutable, perhaps—in the way that a union organizer does something. But a relation is just a relation, not an agent. The bare recognition that there are relations between things that obtain only in virtue of the way they are organized provides neither a science nor the foundation of one. Put another way, we can say that the concept of organization itself plays no role within a science. The same can be said also for the concepts "whole," "organic unity," "hierarchical organization," etc.

Nevertheless, there is a "problem of organization." This is the problem of subjecting to scientific treatment systems which are highly complex with respect to any of a set of theories which are known to be applicable to the systems. The problem for philosophy of science is to understand and formulate whatever special methods, e.g., of concept formation or explanation, are developed

[1] Woodger, *Biological Principles,* pp. 289–90.

in the pursuit of this task. This seems to me the only final way to show that the organismic biologist is correct in his insistence on the right to a "free biology, with concepts and laws of its own." An examination of the function of these concepts, and any logical peculiarities in these laws, incidentally may be of aid in specifying the respects in which biology differs, in points of method, from the other natural sciences.

We must first recapitulate briefly what has been said, and implied, about levels of analysis.

A "level of analysis" is a methodological conception: the world is not constituted of neatly separated strata that force certain distinctions upon anyone who observes it without preconceptions. Rather, bits of the world break into strata when a class of phenomena are approached by an investigator equipped with a set of concepts. In the Kantian terminology, the stratified character of some systems is constituted by the nature of the conceptions through which they are known. Of course, I am not maintaining that the concepts are a priori in any sense.

A level of analysis is defined by a set of concepts related by analytic and synthetic principles of inference. Roughly speaking, the analytic principles are relations of entailment holding between one concept and another, e.g., "X is an atom" entails "X has mass," which entails "X has inertial properties." On a higher level of analysis, we could say "X is an escape reaction" entails "There is a sign of danger," which in turn entails "There is a living organism." The synthetic principles are generalizations, which may indeed be only rough statements of tendency, or may be universal laws, e.g., "Solid bodies may be rigid," or Newton's laws of motion. On the higher level we have principles such as "Signs of danger are associated with predators," "Related animals have similar escape reactions."

The concepts of science and everyday language are not segregated into neat packages, however. Chemistry does not dispense with the concepts of thermodynamics and quantum mechanics, nor does biology dispense with the concepts of either physics or chemistry. It is misleading therefore to say that the phenomena of life are not physical or chemical phenomena: some are and some are not.

The problem of the selection of a level of analysis can arise when a set of phenomena is not understood, not merely in the sense of not explained, but also in the sense that the investigator cannot find his way about; he does not see clearly which problems are significant, or indeed just how he should formulate his questions. Under these conditions the scientists may succumb to two temptations: one is the indulgence in methodology; the other is to honor and cherish principles which have already been established and concepts of proved utility—principles and concepts which are known to apply to the systems under consideration but which are not known to apply to the phenomena which have occasioned the trouble.

Organismic biology is not above temptation, for it yields to the former one; it sternly resists the latter, however. No criticism of either methodology or a reductionist point of view is intended here. It is a tautology to say that these procedures ought not to be practiced excessively, but it would require a peculiar degree of arrogance to say that either of these two activities carried beyond just such-and-such a point is "excessive."

The organismic biologist's methodology is in fact aimed at subverting the latter temptation. He insists upon taking organization, function, and history seriously, and this consists in the development and employment of special concepts and laws. I have maintained that this methodology is sound, but I do not think that in general the writings of the organismic biologists establish its soundness. This statement is of course much too broad to prove without a lengthy excursus into their writings, which I shall not undertake. But their pattern of argument is not adapted to the end: dissection of reductionist theories shows at best that particular theories are inadequate, not that a type of theory is inadequate. Nor, for reasons I have presented, is the "impassable gulf" argument decisive. For the rest, the organismic biologists' metaphysical arguments must be judged indecisive.[2] But there is a way to demonstrate the soundness of a methodological proposal, viz., by showing that it is in fact

[2] The metaphysical arguments occur regularly in the works of organismic biologists I have cited; but see especially, Agar, *Living Organism*, chaps. I and III; and Lillie, *General Biology*, pp. 161–93.

successful. This means that one must see exactly what is the content of the proposal, and then evaluate existing practices in its light. I think that the arguments of this study bear in general and in detail upon these problems, because they are attempts to interpret the biologist's practice in dealing with those features of biological subject matter which have occasioned the organismic biologist's methodology. The task of the present chapter is to demonstrate this thesis; or, in other words, to apply the preceding arguments specifically to the problem of organization and its treatment.

A GENERALIZED CONCEPT OF ORGANIZATION

We have stated what it means to say that one phenomenon p_1, or a class of phenomena P_1, is on a higher level of organization than another class of phenomena P_2. This definition was offered in terms of systems and their parts. It will now be desirable to offer a generalization of this definition of organization that was already implicit in our discussion of teleological analysis, which takes into account temporal organization of activities. Suppose we have a system s that exhibits a phenomenon p over a time interval; and suppose that p is exhaustively divisible into a sequence of phenomena $q_1, q_2, \ldots, q_n$ each taking place in a subinterval of the interval of p. Then p is on a higher level of organization than any q_j with respect to a set G of properties if, when p possesses a property in G, no q_j possesses a property in G. This definition is precisely analogous to the earlier definition of levels of organization in a system and its parts; both are relativized with respect to a class of phenomena or properties. In the present case, however, no special stipulation need be made about the dependence of p on the q's, since, by definition, each q_j is a temporal part of p, and is thus necessary for the occurrence of p. Of course, no phenomenon is at a higher level of organization than its temporal parts with respect to all its properties.

We shall now raise explicitly the question of the relation of levels of organization in the sense of these definitions to the so-called "problem of organization" of the organismic biologists.

In the past the question of organization has been linked to the question of the nature of emergent properties. This is a pity. It is difficult enough to specify clearly what is meant by emergence, but even if a satisfactory explication is possible, no methodological doctrines depend upon the question of whether emergent properties exist. Whether they do or do not, no one will deny the a priori feasibility of seeking interconnections between properties on the higher levels of organization; and no one should deny the feasibility of seeking "reductive" explanations, since, from the point of view of the logic of particular explanations, unexplained and inexplicable connections between systems and their parts are in the same category. To use an example from Rashevsky's model, we might not be able to explain (whether in practice or in principle makes no difference) why the activity of one neuron in a net is accompanied by a cold and another by a hot sensation, but we can certainly explain, having made the necessary correlations, in terms of activities in the net, why, e.g., a cold follows a hot sensation under given circumstances. In short, if we know enough to know that a property is emergent, we will know enough to link it with lower-level properties by means of special coordinating hypotheses.

The search for emergence is simply one aspect of the search for an impassable gulf between the living and the dead. It is motivated by a desire to justify a measure of autonomy in biological theory. But no such justification is needed, and even an absolutely irrefutable demonstration of the existence of emergence adds no support to the cause of justification.

The question of methodological interest is not whether a higher-level phenomenon is in addition an emergent one, but the precise ways in which the fact that it is a higher level is reflected in the logic of its explanation, and the relation between concepts and principles applied to different levels of organization exhibited in the same system.

THE "PROBLEM" OF HISTORICITY

The so-called "problems" of historicity and teleology which have been of so much concern to the organismic biologist are in part special cases of the general problem of organization. Let us first consider historicity.

Suppose that a system exhibits a particular property in the present, e.g., a prospective potency or a competence, but does not exhibit other properties, describable in terms of the concepts customarily employed in describing the system, and also exhibited in the present, that can be systematically linked to the original property. Then the biologist may introduce the notion of a historical system if the property can be systematically correlated with a sequence of events that occurred in the past. If one wishes, the procedure can be described as specification of the state of the system in terms of past occurrences. The case is analogous to the failure to find a parameter, measurable in the present, that can be systematically correlated with, e.g., rate of extinction of a conditioned response in the white rat, but success in correlating this parameter with a history of reinforcement; or failure to predict the melting point of a colloidal gel except in terms of the history of its past heat treatment.

In biological theory it is often possible to construct model-explanations of the behavior of a system with the aid of a theory of systems at a lower level of organization, but only if the state of the lower-level system is historically specified. A special case of such historical specification, I have argued, consists in the performance of a genetic analysis; another consists in the utilization of historical concepts in the state-description. There are two advantages to the latter procedure which are fully exploited by the biologist. First, the definitions of the historical concepts provide rules for determining their applicability, i.e., they allow the scientist to bring to bear, in the particular case, all the criteria of historical relevance, and justify the use of any sort of historical evidence. Second, it eliminates, in some measure, the element of brute fact in a law. Accordingly, a law employing historical concepts, although it might yet lack explanation, is already on the road to explanation. Recall the earlier example of a law employing historical concepts: "Allotetraploids do not cross with either ancestral species." Compare this law with a hypothetical analogue "Organisms with properties A, B, and C do not cross with organisms with properties X, Y, and Z," where the corresponding terms of both laws are assumed to be extensionally identical. The analogue contains elements of brute fact in two distinct ways: the extensional identity of subject and subject, predicate and predicate, and the constant conjunction of A, B, and C with X, Y, and Z. If the analogue is unexplained, i.e., if A, B, and C, and X, Y, and Z do not occur in higher-level hypotheses from which it is deducible, then the original historical law is more fundamental. This means that the probability is higher that the extensions of the historical concepts group together systems containing the factors which could be mentioned in an explanation of the law. Moreover, the historical concept serves as a rule directing the selection of effective nonhistorical criteria of application of the concept. If the historical law is true, using these criteria will never lead the scientist astray, and they may finally lead him to an effective method of identifying instances of the historical concept by reference to those factors which will provide an explanation of the law. This is in fact what happened in the model-explanation of the present law.

These features of historical laws represent one aspect of the use of higher-level concepts that has, to my knowledge, not been noticed by the organismic biologists. For here we see that the employment of concepts in a historical law L which are higher level with respect to the concepts in a theory T capable of explaining L is not only perfectly legitimate in its own right, but, in addition, the particular form of the concepts in L—i.e., historical in W-definition, nonhistorical in E- or E_k-definition—serves an important methodological function. These concepts are the instruments that aid in relating L and T, and though they of course cannot guarantee the explanation of L in terms of T, the historical concepts indicate the broad outlines of a path that cannot lead to error.

The historical concepts of genetics and selection theory—hybrid, polyploid, rudiment, relict, recapitulation, etc.,—together with the groups of the taxonomic system provide the clearest illustration of these points. Taxa provide us with a paradigm of groups of systems whose effective definitions are directed by a historical criterion —the ideal requirement that all taxa be monophyletic at the species level. Following the criterion may lead to a species-description (an E-definition) in terms of morphological or other properties that have nothing whatever to do with laws written about the species.

The requirement of monophyly directs the formation of such E-definitions and checks any wrong moves that might make the effective choice of members diverge from the class of organisms for which the laws hold.

THE "PROBLEM" OF TELEOLOGY

For most organismic biologists, it is not organization at large that is of primary interest, but a special type of organization, namely, the integration, coordination, and purposiveness that enable living systems to develop, persist, and reproduce themselves. In discussing these points organismic biologists are especially prone to obscure metaphysics and mysterious formulae, e.g., the part acts in relation to the whole; the whole acts in reference to an end; the whole determines the part; the end determines the act; the part (act) cannot be understood except in terms of the whole (end); and so on. I think that these formulae can be interpreted in such a way that they are seen to be both true and important, if we attend closely to the logic of functional concepts and analysis and teleological explanation.

I have maintained that the primary theoretical significance of functional analysis lies in the fact that it aids in the selection of levels of analysis and in the implementation of concept formation, appropriate for the treatment of higher-level biological phenomena. I think everyone would agree that this is one use of functional analysis. And I think that one reason why the point is overlooked in discussions of teleology is simply the fact that much functional analysis in biological theory is so easy, and is in fact the result of a kind of second nature that we bring to biology from the affairs of everyday life. This gives functional analysis its taint of anthropomorphism. We commonly describe the actions of our fellow men in reference to further actions to which they contribute, and only secondarily, I would suggest, do we ascribe them to the agency of motive and intent. It is equally a matter of habit to ascribe functions to the activities of two fish—one swimming swiftly toward a hole, the other, fully equipped with a gaping jaw and rows of sharp teeth, following in its path. So far we have, admittedly, only an analogy between these actions and similar human actions which we know subserve ends-in-view, e.g., a Saracen fleeing from a sword-wielding Crusader. If one stops the examination of functional analysis at this point, it is easy to conclude that functional analysis is no more than the application of concepts on the basis of an analogy with human experience, and thus likely to embody the pathetic fallacy. But the functional analysis does accomplish something more. We are, for example, now able to speak significantly of predators and prey. One would not be likely to condemn the use of these concepts, for can we not form logically unexceptionable generalizations with their help? Would an ecologist dispense with them willingly? The concepts "predator" and "prey" of course belong to a special level of analysis—one which is very high with respect to physical and chemical theory. The concepts themselves presuppose functional analysis, and their application in this context requires a functional analysis on this occasion. The analysis places the phenomenon on the biological map, among the huge class of concepts and principles which are related in the same way to other functional analyses. It may be quite true that to apply the concepts in this case is not much help; it doesn't explain either fish's actions. But functional analyses are not explanations, and there is always more involved in an explanation than the application of concepts. The question then is whether or not concepts which require functional analysis for their application do occur in laws capable of use in explanations. This is not an a priori question; it demands attention to the practice of biologists. I have previously maintained that there are such concepts and laws; the best examples are afforded by taxonomy and selection theory.

There must exist a true functional analysis in order for any functional concept to be applied appropriately. But functional analysis can aid in the formation of nonfunctional concepts and in the construction of subsidiary hypotheses in model-explanations. The whole language of perception in psychological theory and in ethology, as against the language of stimulus and response, owes its peculiarities to functional analysis. As all writers on this topic have emphasized, a characteristic of purposive action is its plasticity: this necessarily means that we are able to identify, by some criterion, a certain regularity (of direction or outcome or tendency) that is exhibited under a variety of conditions—otherwise "plasticity" has no meaning. In the case of animal behavior this means that we are able to specify a particular action as belonging to a class of actions by reference to some properties other than the detailed movements of the animal; this is usually done by reference to the constancy or regular change of some spatial relation between the animal and an external object or objects. The explanation of such actions needs to refer to these objects, but must be general enough to account for the behavior in all its plasticity. The hunting wasp catches the bee in flight by an infinite variety of sequences of movements, and in a variety of conditions of illumination; one does not attempt to correlate movement with light stimuli, but says simply that the wasp perceives the bee. The stimulus concept is already stretched when we speak of sign-stimuli or sign-gestalt stimuli; it is already abandoned when we speak of cues. And when an ethologist calls the zigzag mating dance of a stickleback a response to the stimulus "female stickleback with swollen belly" he is merely bowing in the direction of a terminology adapted to a method not adequate to his purposes.

Plasticity is identified in reference to environmental objects. These objects are usually, though not necessarily always, related to plastic behavior by functional analysis. The language which is used in relating behavior to external objects is an amalgam of teleological expressions and the language of perception.[3] It is merely a short step from concepts like "prey" and "predator" to "escape," "warning," "flight," etc., and, to use the contemporary jargon, these concepts have inference-licenses attached; e.g., if an animal "flees" in the presence of "danger," it "perceives" the "predator" as a "threat." It is always feasible to translate away an isolated bit of teleological language, but to eliminate all teleological language is to reject a level of analysis, and, moreover, a level at which phenomena are real. Functional concepts are no more mere useful fictions than are concepts at lower levels of organization.

The language in which we describe behavior which is purposive

---

[3] Agar and Russell both argue in favor of the use of a psychological terminology in the description of purposive behavior. Agar, *Living Organism*, pp. 114–17; and Russell, *Behaviour of Animals*, pp. 166–90.

with respect to a goal is a part of the more general language which is applied in the description of actions, processes, mechanisms, structures, etc., which is functional with respect to a biological end. The general problem is to find concepts which (1) possess as their extensions entities which are functional units, i.e., which do in fact contribute to the achievement of a goal or the fulfillment of an end; and (2) which facilitate the formation of the widest generalizations. Of course, the theoretical terms of physics, chemistry, physiology, and genetics meet these requirements: various levers in the human body, genes, even atoms are functional units. The problem of organization arises when we try to discriminate functional units with a complex spatial or temporal structure.

The units depend for their functional activity upon their parts and the relations among them, but it may be the case that the units' activities *qua* functional are higher level with respect to the activities of their parts, and that there are regularities among such functional units that are not shown by their parts. The probability of the latter contingency is increased by the fact that the same function can be served by what appears, when considered at a lower level of analysis, as a number of kinds of actions. It may even be the case that the set of concepts which are often or customarily employed in description of systems or activities that do act as functional units signify a set of properties G no subset of which is both a necessary and sufficient condition for the application of a concept of higher level. If such concepts are E-defined by reference to properties in G, they are fully polytypic with respect to G. I have suggested that some morphological concepts are fully polytypic with respect to the set of structural properties, i.e., many of those properties which are usually termed "morphological," and that some ethological concepts are fully polytypic with respect to every descriptive property of animal behavior except relational properties which relate behavior to external objects.

When the utility of a concept in generalizations is dependent upon the functional activities of the members of its extensions, the biologist may be unwilling to commit himself to a definition of the concept in terms of properties G that have no explicable connection with the functions, i.e., with properties appropriate to a level of analysis below the level of the functional activity. If, however, the concept is in practice E-defined by properties in G, it is polytypic, but may not be fully polytypic. Such concepts are common in biological theory. The systematic groups, or taxa, are polytypic with respect to the set of morphological properties employed in their effective description.

In the somewhat vague sense in which the atom is the fundamental unit of chemical activity, the functional unit is fundamental within the theory of evolution. The roles of functional analysis and teleological explanation in selection theory have been outlined; we need only add here that the concepts used in the description of evolutionary change are higher level with respect to the concepts of genetic theory, which, together with the laws of genetics, provide much of the preestablished theory for selectionist explanations.

The distinction which was drawn between the "field" and the "subject" of a model was intended to underline the use of models in explanation of higher-level phenomena. In interlevel models, the primary subject-descriptions concern phenomena which are on a lower level of organization than the field phenomena. One aspect of these models is the introduction of subsidiary hypotheses connecting higher- and lower-level concepts, e.g., special hypotheses connecting the activity of neural elements with the occurrence of sensations, or the presence of a particular gene with a mode of embryological development.

On the whole, it must be admitted that the concepts which have been developed through functional analysis for description of phenomena at the higher levels of organization have not as yet proved of much help in the formulation of scientific deductive systems of a power and fruitfulness comparable to those found in regions of physics, chemistry, and even parts of biology. It should be emphasized that neither a functional analysis nor a teleological explanation is a teleological law. Braithwaite does speak of hierarchical arrangements of teleological laws such that the laws on the lower levels are deductive consequences of the higher-level laws,[4] but I have been unable to reconstruct such a hierarchy, and Braithwaite does not give a concrete example. I think he is inclined to see

[4] Braithwaite, *Scientific Explanation*, pp. 339–40.

a deductive system in what is merely a hierarchy of functional relations, e.g., Tinbergen's behavior hierarchy for the stickleback. But
the past failure to find such laws does not mean a future failure, nor
does absence of theories of this particular logical structure mean
absence of all theory. I have maintained that a theory can be a
family of models and that selection theory is in fact of this character. Theories are instruments for dealing with their subject matter,
but they are also instruments for their own perfection. Models, in
so far as they yield explanations, facilitate directly the former function, and, in so far as they yield only quasi-explanations, they directly contribute to the latter function.

ORGANISMIC BIOLOGY AS METHODOLOGY

We shall now examine some of the organismic biologists' pro-
nouncements concerning the relation of part and whole, activity and
goal or end. A single principle allows us, so it appears to me, to
convert their cryptic formulae into methodological proposals. Less
sympathetic interpretations tend to convert them, I fear, into truisms or unproved assumptions. Consider first the part-whole relation. The organismic biologist's position has been summarized in
the following ways: "The whole acts as a causal unit . . . on its
own parts";[5] "The living body and its physiological environment
form an organic whole, the parts of which cannot be understood in
separation from one another";[6] "The organism in its totality is as
essential to an explanation of its elements as its elements are to
an explanation of the organism";[7] and "No part of any organism can
be rightly interpreted except as part of any individual organism, this
individual in turn being interpreted as a member of a taxonomic
group."[8]

It is sometimes proposed that these and similar statements be interpreted in terms of the function of self-maintenance. It is pointed
out that organisms do maintain themselves through a vastly complex
system of minutely adjusted parts, and that "understanding the part
in terms of the whole" simply means understanding what role the

[5] Agar, *Living Organism*, p. 2.   [6] Haldane, *Mechanism*, p. 80.
[7] This, according to Ritter, is the central thesis of his two-volume work.
Unity of the Organism, I, 24.
[8] *Ibid.*, II, 93.

part plays in maintenance of the whole living organism. And this is certainly a point that organismic biologists acknowledge. Indeed, they insist upon it. But everyone would agree about the facts of self-maintenance, and, as Haldane points out, the strength of "mechanism" has in large measure rested on the discovery of self-regulating mechanisms.[9] In any case, self-maintenance lends no special support to organismic biology. On this interpretation, accordingly, the quoted formulae turn out to be truisms.

A second interpretation, presented by Woodger with characteristic care and rigor, may be summarized as follows. An organic part *in situ* exhibits activities of a kind that it does not exhibit in an abnormal environment. The normal environment (which, although Woodger does not say so, may include, by recursion, the whole organism) is causally involved in these activities, and we cannot expect to learn about these activities other than by studying them *in situ*.[10] The first two clauses of this doctrine are certainly noncontroversial. Evidently a kidney cell, for example, will not excrete urine in a culture medium; the hand will not grasp objects if severed from the muscles that flex and extend its joints. So far the doctrine is a truism, but perhaps the kind of truism, like the law of excluded middle, that people are, under some circumstances, perversely willing to challenge. The last clause is, however, the core of the doctrine, and it seems to be based upon a misunderstanding. It is certainly unproved. To demonstrate the misunderstanding, let p be an organic part, and W the whole of which it is a part. The final clause states that p shows activities in W that we could not discover by studying p while not in W. But failure to study p in W is not the same thing as studying p in isolation; it merely means that p is being studied as a part of other wholes, i.e., in other contexts. And the total experience of science is witness to the fact that the study of an element in some contexts may provide a theory for prediction of its behavior in other contexts. The theory of chemical valences is the example usually cited in this connection: one can predict, e.g., the combining weights of silver and chlorine

[9] Haldane, *Mechanism*, p. 13.
[10] Woodger, *Biological Principles*, pp. 314–15.

by studying them "in isolation" from each other; one merely determines their valences and atomic weights.

I would propose the following interpretation of the organismic biologist's position on this point. Eliminating the "cannot" and "essential" as unnecessary exaggerations, the organismic biologist is proposing that we describe the parts of organic wholes in their activities *qua* parts by employing concepts that are defined by reference to the higher-level phenomena exhibited by the whole, or at least by larger segments of the whole.

The same phenomenon, as we have observed, can be described in a variety of ways. The organismic biologist is proposing that we describe the phenomena exhibited by organic parts in explicit relation to the phenomena exhibited by the wholes, or large systems, of which they are parts, i.e., that we apply to parts concepts defined in terms of phenomena that these parts do not exhibit. This is not a paradoxical proposal. Such concepts are in fact common in everyday speech and in the language of technology. "Banker," for example, is a term applied to individual men, but it is defined in terms of the phenomena shown by a larger system of which the man is a part. A bias resistor does not show the activity in terms of which the concept is defined, *viz.*, establishing a potential difference between the grid and cathode of a vacuum tube. Nor is it a trivial proposal, since there are clear and widely practiced alternatives. Moreover, these alternatives seem to have been actually recommended by the "mechanists" and "elementalists" who constitute the classical foe of organismic biology. Among these alternatives are defining a part in terms of its constituents, e.g., chemical ingredients, cellular parts, etc., and the physical and chemical parts of these ingredients; in terms of shapes, colors, measurable magnitudes, etc.; in short, in terms of properties which the part could in fact possess if it were not a part of the whole in question. The point of view is of course a proposal to attend to relational properties of a special type, and to employ concepts defined by reference to them, wherever possible, in the formulation of generalizations. The proposal can only be justified, finally, by its success in yielding generalizations.

Perhaps two positions which the organismic biologist is not maintaining should be distinguished here. He is not merely maintaining that the properties of a part of a system are determined by properties of the whole system. This is in general true of all systems, with respect to some properties. For example, the potential at a point in an electrostatic system is determined by the distribution of charges in the whole system, but in this case the concept "potential at a point" is not defined in terms of the distribution of charges in its neighborhood, but simply as the work done in moving a unit charge from a great distance to the point. Nor is he saying that we may explain phenomena at a lower level of organization by reference to phenomena exhibited at a higher level; this is impossible by definition, since higher-level laws are not exemplified in lower-level systems, and a law cannot explain the behavior of systems in which it is not exemplified.

Functional concepts are the clearest examples of such concepts which answer to this proposal. We have already discussed the ways in which they are useful, so the organismic biologist's position seems well taken to that extent. All such concepts are not functional, however; "epidermis," for example, is not functional, but it is defined by reference to a larger whole.

An interesting consequence of this interpretation is that the language we employ in describing machines largely conforms to the organismic biologist's proposal. The parts of machines, e.g., cams, pinions, bobs, flywheels, etc., are often designated by functional concepts. Though this would seem odd to an organismic biologist, it is not surprising. This language is so designed that casual talk about machines conveys as much information as possible about the workings of the machine, since this, and not its material constitution, color, etc., is our primary interest.

The essence of the interpretation is this: I suggest that for "The whole determines the part," and similar formulae, we read "The concept of the whole determines the concept of the part."

The same principle yields an analogous interpretation of the organismic biologist's position on the relation of activities to their goal or end. He is maintaining that we may consider the end served or goal attained by an activity in formulating the concepts in terms of which we describe the activity. This procedure also typically yields functional concepts, but not always. It may yield concepts defined in terms of objects related to the goal achieved. I have maintained that a distinguishing feature of teleological explanation is the occurrence in the *explanans* of an explicit reference to the goal, or to some variable effectively defined in terms of the goal. In this way the reference to a goal provides the conceptual materials for a type of model-explanation, and thus contains a latent reference to a level of organization above the level exhibited in the subject of the model.

Conclusion

Every attempt has been made in this study to give sympathetic consideration to the suggestions of organismic biology, but any by-paths which were discovered in the course of the investigation have been explored, with the result that the study possesses some emphases that are in a sense antithetical to the organismic point of view. I have given no privileged status to the organismic level of organization, and I am sure that most organismic biologists would think that the use of models, in the sense in which the term has been employed, is not the way to approach the problem of higher-level phenomena. I have indicated why I think this suspicion is unfounded. In addition, I have throughout denied the intrinsic irreducibility of organic to inorganic phenomena; but in any case the organismic biologists are divided on this point. Finally, I think that the analysis of the uses of functional, historical, and polytypic concepts, in particular the concepts of the systematic groups, and the use of functional analysis and teleological explanation are all perfectly consonant with the organismic biologist's general methodology, and serve to relate this methodology to the practice of other biologists.

Bibliography

Agar, W. E. *A Contribution to the Theory of the Living Organism.* 2d ed. Melbourne, Australia: Melbourne University Press, 1951.

Altschul, Eugen, and Erwin Biser. "The Validity of Unique Mathematical Models in Science," *Philosophy of Science,* XV (January, 1948), 13–14.

Arber, Agnes. *The Mind and the Eye: A Study of the Biologist's Standpoint.* Cambridge: Cambridge University Press, 1954.

Arkell, W. J., and J. A. Moy-Thomas. "Palaeontology and the Taxonomic Problem," in *The New Systematics.* Edited by Julian Huxley. Oxford: Clarendon Press, 1940.

Ashby, W. R. "The Nervous System as Physical Machine: With Special Reference to the Origin of Adaptive Behaviour," *Mind,* LVI (January, 1947), 46.

Bather, F. A. "Biological Classification, Past and Future," *Quarterly Journal of the Geological Society,* LXXXIII (1927), ci.

Berg, L. S. *Nomogenesis, or Evolution Determined by Law.* Translated by J. N. Rostovtsow. London: Constable & Co., 1926.

Bergmann, Gustav. "On Some Methodological Problems of Psychology," *Philosophy of Science,* Vol. VII (1940). Reprinted in *Readings in the Philosophy of Science.* Edited by Herbert Feigl and May Brodbeck. New York: Appleton-Century-Crofts, Inc., 1953.

—— "Psychoanalysis and Experimental Psychology: A Review from the Standpoint of Scientific Empiricism," *Mind,* LII (1943), 122–40. Reprinted in *Psychological Theory.* Edited by Melvin H. Marx. New York: Macmillan Co., 1951.

Blum, Harold F. *Time's Arrow and Evolution.* Princeton: Princeton University Press, 1951.

Braithwaite, Richard Bevan. *Scientific Explanation.* Cambridge: Cambridge University Press, 1953.

—— "Teleological Explanations," in *Proceedings of the Aristotelian Society,* N.S., Vol. XLVII (1947).

Broad, C. D. *The Mind and Its Place in Nature.* Sixth Impression. London: Routledge & Kegan Paul Ltd., 1951.

Burma, Benjamin H. "The Species Concept: A Semantic Review," *Evolution,* III (December, 1949), 369–70.

Calman, W. T. "A Museum Zoologist's View of Taxonomy," in *The New Systematics*. Edited by Julian Huxley. Oxford: Clarendon Press, 1940.

Carnap, Rudolf. "Testability and Meaning," *Philosophy of Science*, III (1936), 419–71, and IV (1937), 1–40. Reprinted in *Readings in the Philosophy of Science*. Edited by Herbert Feigl and May Brodbeck. New York: Appleton-Century-Crofts, Inc., 1953.

Darlington, C. D. "Taxonomic Species and Genetic Systems," in *The New Systematics*. Edited by Julian Huxley. Oxford: Clarendon Press, 1940.

De Beer, Gavin Rylands. *Embryology and Evolution*. Oxford: Clarendon Press, 1930.

De Beer, Gavin Rylands (ed.). *Evolution*. Oxford: Clarendon Press, 1938.

Deutsch, Karl W. "Mechanism, Teleology, and Mind," *Philosophy and Phenomenological Research*, XII (December, 1951), 200.

Dobzhansky, Theodosius. *Evolution, Genetics, and Man*. New York: John Wiley & Sons, Inc., 1955.

—— *Genetics and the Origin of Species*. New York: Columbia University Press, 1937.

Feigl, Herbert, and May Brodbeck (eds.). *Readings in the Philosophy of Science*. New York: Appleton-Century-Crofts, Inc., 1953.

Feigl, Herbert, and Wilfrid Sellars (eds.). *Readings in Philosophical Analysis*. New York: Appleton-Century-Crofts, Inc., 1949.

Fisher, R. A. *The Genetical Theory of Natural Selection*. Oxford: Clarendon Press, 1930.

—— "Retrospect of the Criticisms of Natural Selection," in *Evolution as a Process*. Edited by Julian Huxley, A. C. Hardy, and E. B. Ford. London: George Allen & Unwin, Ltd., 1945.

Fothergill, Philip G. *Historical Aspects of Evolution*. London: Hollis & Carter, 1952.

Gallie, W. B. "Explanations in History and the Genetic Sciences," *Mind*, LXIV (April, 1955), 161–67.

Gasking, Douglas. "Causation and Recipes," *Mind*, LXIV (October, 1955), 486–87.

Gilmour, J. S. L. "Taxonomy and Philosophy," in *The New Systematics*. Edited by Julian Huxley. Oxford: Clarendon Press, 1940.

Goldschmidt, Richard. *The Material Basis of Evolution*. New Haven: Yale University Press, 1940.

Gregg, John R. *The Language of Taxonomy*. New York: Columbia University Press, 1954.

—— "Taxonomy, Language, and Reality," *American Naturalist*, LXXXIV (November–December, 1950), 421–33.

Haeckel, Ernst. *Three Lectures on Evolution*. Girard, Kansas: Appeal Publishing Co., [1905].

Haldane, J. S. *Mechanism, Life, and Personality*. 2d ed. New York: E. P. Dutton & Co., 1923.

—— *The Philosophical Basis of Biology*. London: Hodder & Stoughton Ltd., 1931.

Hempel, Carl G. "The Function of General Laws in History," *Journal of Philosophy*, XXXIX (1942), 35–48. Reprinted in *Readings in Philosophical Analysis*. Edited by Herbert Feigl and Wilfrid Sellars. New York: Appleton-Century-Crofts, Inc., 1949.

Hempel, Carl G., and Paul Oppenheim. "The Logic of Explanation," *Philosophy of Science*, XV (1948), 135–75. Reprinted in *Readings in the Philosophy of Science*. Edited by Herbert Feigl and May Brodbeck. New York: Appleton-Century-Crofts, Inc., 1953.

Hofstadter, Albert. "Objective Teleology," *Journal of Philosophy*, XXXVIII (January, 1941), No. 2, 29–39.

Huxley, Julian. "Introductory: Towards the New Systematics," in *The New Systematics*. Edited by Julian Huxley. Oxford: Clarendon Press, 1940.

—— *Problems of Relative Growth*. New York: Dial Press, 1932.

Huxley, Julian (ed.). *The New Systematics*. Oxford: Clarendon Press, 1940.

Huxley, Julian, A. C. Hardy, and E. B. Ford (eds.). *Evolution as a Process*. London: George Allen & Unwin, Ltd., 1945.

Lillie, Ralph Stayner. *General Biology and Philosophy of Organism*. Chicago: University of Chicago Press, 1945.

McDougall, William. *Outline of Psychology*. New York: Charles Scribner's Sons, 1923.

Mace, C. A. "Mechanical and Teleological Causation," in *Proceedings of the Aristotelian Society*, Supplementary Vol. XIV (1935). Reprinted in Readings in Philosophical Analysis. Edited by Herbert Feigl and Wilfrid Sellars. New York: Appleton-Century-Crofts, Inc., 1949.

Madden, Edward H. "The Philosophy of Science in Gestalt Theory," *Philosophy of Science*, XIX (1952), 228–39. Reprinted in *Readings in the Philosophy of Science*. Edited by Herbert Feigl and May Brodbeck. New York: Appleton-Century-Crofts, Inc., 1953.

Mainx, Felix. *Foundations of Biology*. (International Encyclopedia of Unified Science, Vol. I, No. 9.) Chicago: University of Chicago Press, 1955.

Marx, Melvin H. (ed.). *Psychological Theory*. New York: Macmillan Co., 1951.

Mayr, Ernst. *Systematics and the Origin of Species*. New York: Columbia University Press, 1942.

Mayr, Ernst, E. Gorton Linsley, and Robert L. Usinger. *Methods and Principles of Systematic Zoology*. New York: McGraw-Hill Book Co., Inc., 1953.

Morgan, Clifford T. *Physiological Psychology*. New York: McGraw-Hill Book Co., Inc., 1943.

Morgan, Thomas Hunt. *Embryology and Genetics*. New York: Columbia University Press, 1934.

Nagel, Ernest. "Mechanistic Explanation and Organismic Biology," *Philosophy and Phenomenological Research*, XI (March, 1951), 330.

—— "Some Issues in the Logic of Historical Analysis," *Scientific Monthly*, LXXIV (March, 1952), No. 3, 163.

—— "Teleological Explanation and Teleological Systems," in *Vision and Action*. Edited by S. Ratner. New Brunswick, N.J.: Rutgers University Press, 1953. Reprinted in *Readings in the Philosophy of Science*. Edited by Herbert Feigl and May Brodbeck. New York: Appleton-Century-Crofts, Inc., 1953.

Needham, J. "Mechanistic Biology and the Religious Consciousness," in *Science, Religion, and Reality*. Edited by J. Needham. New York: George Braziller, Inc., 1955.

Needham, J. (ed.). *Science, Religion, and Reality*. New York: George Braziller, Inc., 1955.

Parker-Rhodes, A. F. Review of John R. Gregg's *The Language of Taxonomy*, in *Philosophical Review*, LXVI (January, 1957), 124.

Perry, Ralph Barton. "A Behavioristic View of Purpose," *Journal of Philosophy*, XVIII (February, 1921), No. 4, 85–105.

—— "Purpose as Systematic Unity," *Monist*, XXVII (July, 1917), 352.

Poincaré, H. *Science and Hypothesis*. New York: Dover Publications, Inc., 1952.

Rashevsky, N. *Mathematical Biophysics*. Chicago: University of Chicago Press, 1948.

Richards, O. W. "The Formation of Species: Methods of Studying the Early Stages of Evolutionary Divergence in Animals," in *Evolution*. Edited by Gavin Rylands De Beer. Oxford: Clarendon Press, 1938.

Ritter, William Emerson. *The Unity of the Organism; or the Organismal Conception of Life*. 2 vols. Boston: Richard G. Badger, Gorham Press, 1919.

Robson, G. C. *The Species Problem*. Edinburgh: Oliver & Boyd, 1928.

Rosenblueth, Arturo, and Norbert Wiener. "The Role of Models in Science," *Philosophy of Science*, XII (October, 1945), 317–20.

Rosenblueth, Arturo, Norbert Wiener, and Julian Bigelow. "Behavior, Purpose and Teleology," *Philosophy of Science*, X (January, 1943), 18–19.

Russell, Edward Stuart. *The Behaviour of Animals*. 2d ed. London: Edward Arnold & Co., 1938.

—— *The Directiveness of Organic Activities*. Cambridge: Cambridge University Press, 1945.

Schroedinger, Erwin. *What Is Life?* Cambridge: Cambridge University Press, 1945.

Simpson, George Gaylord. *The Major Features of Evolution.* New York: Columbia University Press, 1953.

—— *The Meaning of Evolution.* New Haven: Yale University Press, 1952.

—— "The Principles of Classification and a Classification of Mammals," *Bulletin of the American Museum of Natural History,* LXXXV (1945), 1–8.

Skinner, B. F. *The Behavior of Organisms.* New York: Appleton-Century-Crofts, Inc., 1938.

Sommerhoff, George. *Analytical Biology.* London: Oxford University Press, 1950.

Sprague, T. A. "Taxonomic Botany, with Special Reference to the Angiosperms," in *The New Systematics.* Edited by Julian Huxley. Oxford: Clarendon Press, 1940.

Thompson, D'Arcy W. Review of J. S. Haldane's *The New Physiology, Mind,* N.S., XXVII, 359.

Tinbergen, N. *The Study of Instinct.* Oxford: Clarendon Press, 1951.

Toulmin, Stephen. *The Philosophy of Science.* New York: Hutchinson's University Library, 1953.

Von Bertalanffy, Ludwig. *Modern Theories of Development.* London: Oxford University Press, 1933.

—— "An Outline of General Systems Theory," *British Journal for the Philosophy of Science,* I (August, 1950), No. 2, 134–65.

—— *Problems of Life.* New York: John Wiley & Sons, Inc., 1952.

Wheeler, William Morton (ed.). *Essays in Philosophical Biology.* Cambridge: Harvard University Press, 1939.

—— "Present Tendencies in Biological Theory," *Scientific Monthly,* February, 1929. Reprinted in *Essays in Philosophical Biology.* Edited by William Morton Wheeler. Cambridge: Harvard University Press, 1939.

Woodger, J. H. *Biological Principles.* London: Routledge & Kegan Paul Ltd., 1948.

—— *Biology and Language.* Cambridge: Cambridge University Press, 1952.

Wright, Sewall. "The Statistical Consequences of Mendelian Heredity in Relation to Speciation," in *The New Systematics.* Edited by Julian Huxley. Oxford: Clarendon Press, 1940.

Zilsel, Edgar. "Physics and the Problem of Historico-sociological Laws," *Philosophy of Science,* VIII (1941), 567–79. Reprinted in *Readings in the Philosophy of Science.* Edited by Herbert Feigl and May Brodbeck. New York: Appleton-Century-Crofts, Inc., 1953.

Index